keyboard theory

Level 1

By Grace Vandendool

ISBN 0-88797-491-0

FREDERICK
HARRIS
MUSIC

Foreword

KEYBOARD THEORY – Level 1 was written in response to the needs of music students in private and classroom instruction. It attempts to bridge the difficulties students encounter when relating basic music theory to the practical application of learning an instrument.

KEYBOARD THEORY – Level 1 is a ONE VOLUME, fast-moving method intended for older students.

A visual approach—the relationship between theory and the keyboard—is emphasized throughout the series to simplify the learning of new concepts. All explanations and instructions are kept short, simple and easy to understand. Reviews at the end of most chapters, covering current and previously learned concepts, help students to retain and test their knowledge.

A recommended textbook in preparation for writing the exams of The Royal Conservatory of Music and the Western Ontario Conservatory of Music. Recommended for all graded and non-graded systems.

Acknowledgements

I would like to thank the following people for their devoted efforts
in the preparation of this publication:

Editor:	Carol J. McFadden
Music Engraving & Typesetting:	Harry Vandendool
Cover Art:	Neil J. Vandendool

I would like to thank Carolyn Jones for proofreading, and my students
whose enthusiasm and comments were very much appreciated during
the development of this book.

A final thanks goes to my husband and children for their constant
encouragement to write this book.

GRACE VANDENDOOL

To my son-in-law, Gary

Contents

LESSON No. 1

Major Scales

The Sharp Key Signature

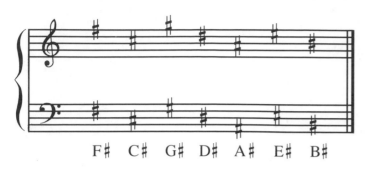

F♯ C♯ G♯ D♯ A♯ E♯ B♯

The **ORDER** of the seven **SHARPS** is:

F♯, C♯, G♯, D♯, A♯, E♯ and B♯.

EXERCISE:

1. Copy the **SEVEN SHARPS** of a key signature in the correct **PLACE** and **ORDER**. Name the **SHARPS**.

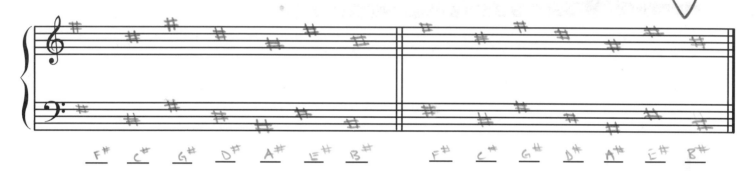

F♯ C♯ G♯ D♯ A♯ E♯ B♯   F♯ C♯ G♯ D♯ A♯ E♯ B♯

The Naming of Sharp Key Signatures

EXAMPLE:

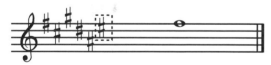

Key: F♯ Major

1. The **LAST SHARP** in the example is **E♯**.
2. A **DIATONIC SEMITONE ABOVE E♯** is the **TONIC NOTE F♯**.
3. Therefore, the name of the **KEY SIGNATURE** is **F♯**.

EXERCISES:

2. Write the **TONIC NOTE** found a diatonic semitone above the last sharp. Name the Major key.

Key: C♯ †   F♯ †   B †   C♯ †   F♯ †   B †

3. Write a **KEY SIGNATURE** for the keys below.

C♯ Major   F♯ Major   B Major   C♯ Major   F♯ Major   B Major

4. Write the following scales ascending and descending in whole notes, using a **KEY SIGNATURE.** Mark the **SEMITONES** with a slur.

a. B Major

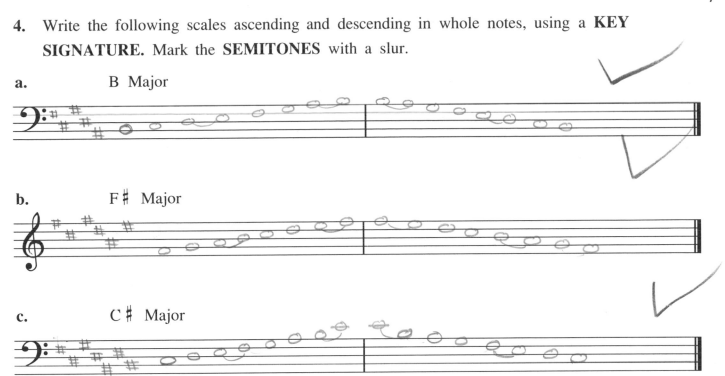

b. F♯ Major

c. C♯ Major

5. Write the following scales ascending and descending in half notes, using **ACCIDENTALS.** (Don't forget the bar lines). Circle and label the **TONIC** notes.

a. F♯ Major in the bass clef

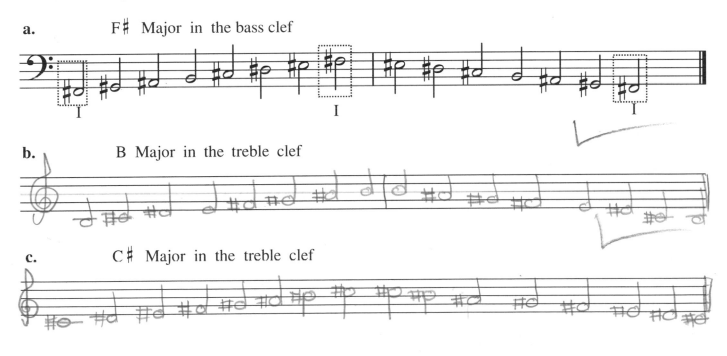

b. B Major in the treble clef

c. C♯ Major in the treble clef

6. Name the **ACCIDENTALS** that make up the following key signatures. Write them in the correct order.

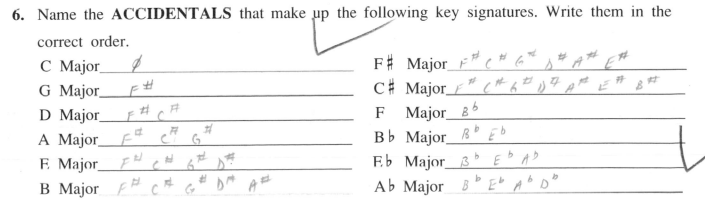

C Major____∅____

G Major____F♯____

D Major____F♯ C♯____

A Major____F♯ C♯ G♯____

E Major____F♯ C♯ G♯ D♯____

B Major____F♯ C♯ G♯ D♯ A♯____

F♯ Major____F♯ C♯ G♯ D♯ A♯ E♯____

C♯ Major____F♯ C♯ G♯ D♯ A♯ E♯ B♯____

F Major____B♭____

B♭ Major____B♭ E♭____

E♭ Major____B♭ E♭ A♭____

A♭ Major____B♭ E♭ A♭ D♭____

The Flat Key Signature

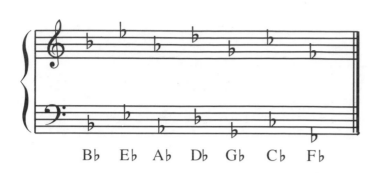

Bb Eb Ab Db Gb Cb Fb

The **ORDER** of the seven **FLATS** is:

Bb, Eb, Ab, Db, Gb, Cb and Fb.

EXERCISE:

7. Copy the **SEVEN FLATS** of a key signature in the correct **PLACE** and **ORDER**.
   Name the **FLATS**.

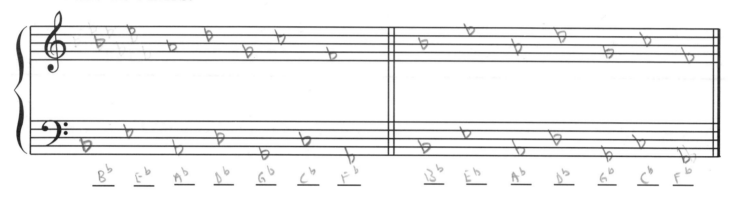

Bb Eb Ab Db Gb Cb Fb   Bb Eb Ab Db Gb Cb Fb

The Naming of Flat Key Signatures

EXAMPLE:

Key: Gb Major

The **SECOND LAST FLAT** in the example is Gb.
Therefore the name of the **KEY SIGNATURE** is Gb.
* The **ONE EXCEPTION** to this rule is **F MAJOR**,
which has only **Bb** in the key signature.

EXERCISES:

8. Write the **TONIC NOTE** and name the **MAJOR KEY.**

Key: Cb Major ___ Gb ___ Db ___ Cb ___ Gb ___ Db ___

9. Write a **KEY SIGNATURE** for the keys below.

Cb Major   Gb Major   Db Major   Cb Major   Gb Major   Db Major

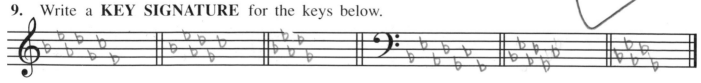

10. Write the following scales ascending and descending in dotted half notes, using a **KEY SIGNATURE.**

   a.   Db Major

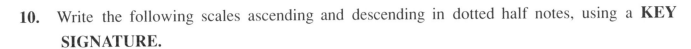

   b.   Gb Major

   c.   Cb Major

11. Write the following scales ascending and descending in quarter notes, using **ACCIDENTALS.** (Don't forget the bar lines.)   Circle and label the **DOMINANT** notes.

   a.   Gb Major in the treble clef

   b.   Db Major in the bass clef

   c.   Cb Major in the bass clef

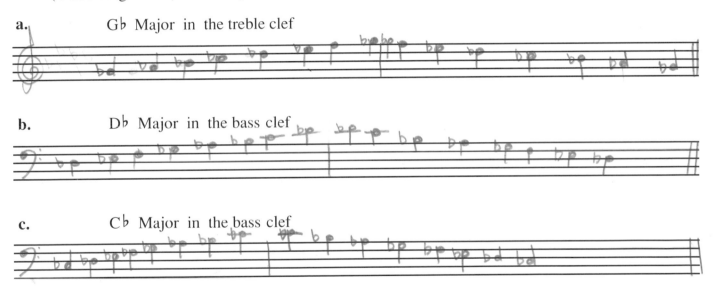

12. Name the **ACCIDENTALS** that make up the following key signatures. Write them in the correct order.

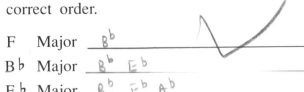

F Major Bb		D Major F# C#
Bb Major Bb Eb		G Major F#
Eb Major Bb Eb Ab		E Major F# C# G# D#
Ab Major Bb Eb Ab Db		A Major F# C# G#
Db Major Bb Eb Ab Db Gb		B Major F# C# G# D# A#
Gb Major Bb Eb Ab Db Gb Cb		F# Major F# C# G# D# A# E#
Cb Major Bb Eb Ab Db Gb Cb Fb		C# Major F# C# G# D# A# E# B#

13. Name the **MAJOR KEY** and write the **DOMINANT NOTE** for each key signature.

a.

Key: _B+_ ____ _B♭+_ ____ _A+_ ____ _D♭+_ ____ _F#+_

b.

Key: _C♭+_ ____ _D+_ ____ _G♭+_ ____ _C#+_ ____ _C♭+_

14. Write a **KEY SIGNATURE** and the **TONIC NOTE** for each key below.

a.

B Major   D♭ Major   F# Major   G Major   E Major

b.

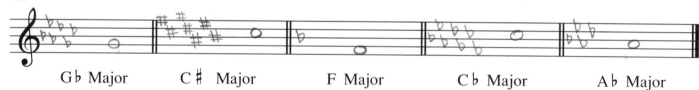

G♭ Major   C# Major   F Major   C♭ Major   A♭ Major

15. Write the following scales, ascending and descending.

a. (B+) the Major scale, with a key signature of **FIVE SHARPS**

b. (G♭+) the Major scale, with a key signature of **SIX FLATS**

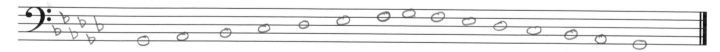

c. (B♭+) the Major scale, with a key signature of **TWO FLATS**

16. Write the following scales **ASCENDING** only, in quarter notes, using a **KEY SIGNATURE.**

a.   C Major

Remember:

C Major has **NO SHARPS** or **FLATS.**

b.   C♯ Major

C♯ Major has **7 SHARPS.**

c.   C♭ Major

C♭ Major has **7 FLATS.**

TRADITIONALY 1/8th Notes are grouped in PAIRS tied Answer in blk

17. Write the following scales **DESCENDING** only, in eighth notes, using **ACCIDENTALS.**

a.   D♭ Major BEADG

d.   B Major F C G D A

b.   A Major

e.   G♭ Major BEADGC

c.   A♭ Major BEAD

f.   E Major

18. Write the following scales **ASCENDING** only, in sixteenth notes, using a **KEY SIGNATURE.**

a.   D Major

c.   E♭ Major

b.   F Major

d.   G Major

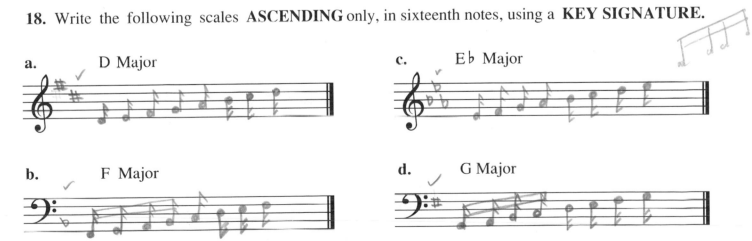

100

15 **1.** Write the following scales ascending and descending in whole notes, using a
KEY SIGNATURE.

Mark the **SEMITONES** with a slur. (Don't forget the centre bar line).

a.   F# Major

b.   Gb Major

c.   B Major

10 **2.** Write **TONIC** triads, using **ACCIDENTALS** for the given keys below.

Db Major   f# minor   Cb Major   C# Major   d minor

10 **3.** Write the following **MELODIC INTERVALS** above the given notes.

minor 6th   Major 7th   Perfect 8th   minor 3rd   Major 2nd

10 **4.** Add a **TIME SIGNATURE** to the beginning of each measure.

13

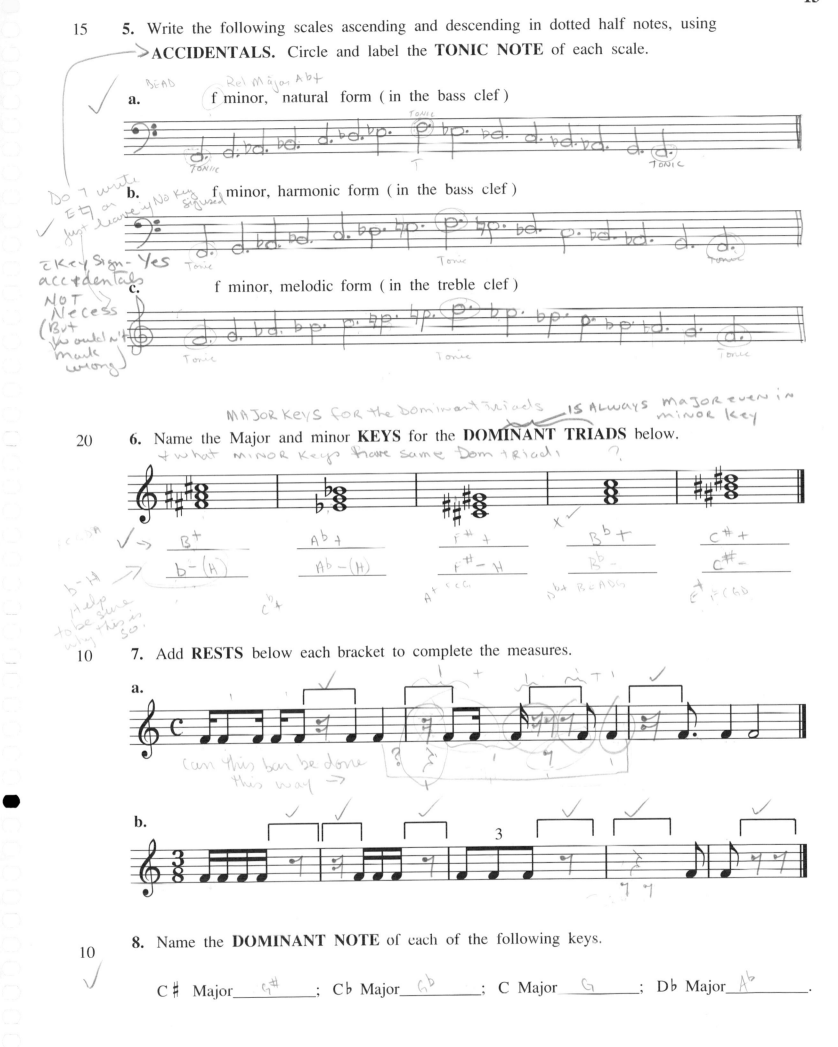

LESSON No. 2

The Double Sharp ("x")

Double sharp notes are played on the white keys with the exception of E✖ and B✖, which are played on the black keys. **NOTICE THAT THE LETTERNAMES ARE NOT CHANGED!**

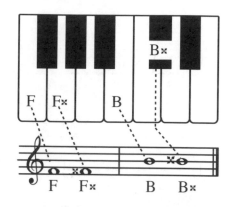

The **DOUBLE SHARP** raises the note by **TWO SEMITONES** (two half steps), or a **WHOLE TONE.**

OR

The **DOUBLE SHARP** raises the **SHARPENED** note by a **CHROMATIC SEMITONE.** Sharpened notes, which become double sharp notes are also played on the white keys, with the exception of E✖ and B✖ , which are played on the black keys

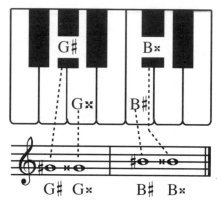

To cancel the double sharp, **LOWER** the **DOUBLE SHARP** note **TWO SEMITONES**, by using a **NATURAL SIGN.**

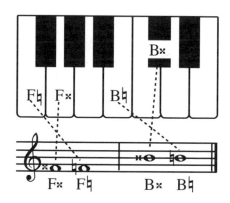

OR

To cancel the double sharp, lower the **DOUBLE SHARP** note by a **CHROMATIC SEMITONE,** by using a **SHARP SIGN.**

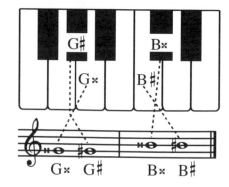

EXERCISES:

1. RAISE each note by a **WHOLE TONE.** Do **NOT** change the letternames.
Draw corresponding lines to the keyboard.

a.

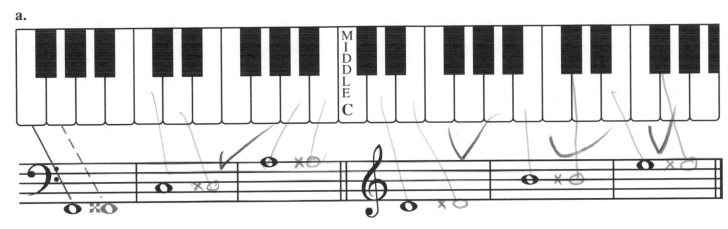

b. RAISE each note by a **CHROMATIC SEMITONE** and draw corresponding lines to the keyboard.

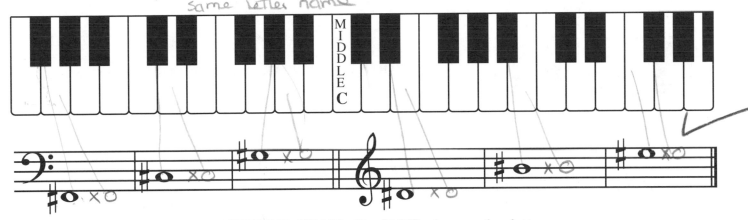

2. LOWER each note by a **WHOLE TONE. Do NOT** change the letternames.
Draw corresponding lines to the keyboard.

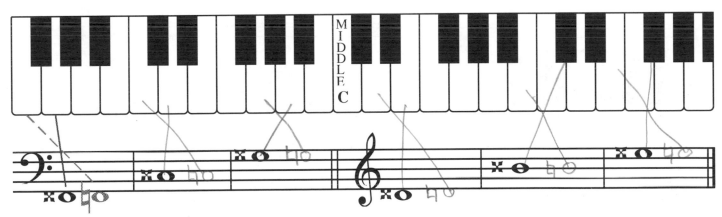

3. LOWER each **DOUBLE SHARP NOTE** by a **CHROMATIC SEMITONE** and draw
corresponding lines to the keyboard.

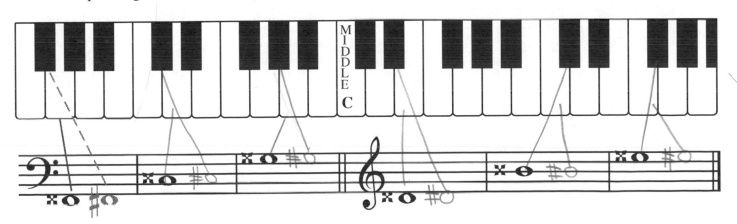

The Double Flat ("♭♭")

Double flat notes are played on the white keys, with the exception of C♭♭ and F♭♭, which are played on the black keys. **NOTICE THAT THE LETTERNAMES ARE NOT CHANGED!**

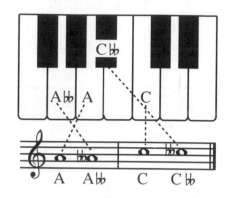

The **DOUBLE FLAT** lowers the note by **TWO SEMITONES** (two half steps), or a **WHOLE TONE.**

OR

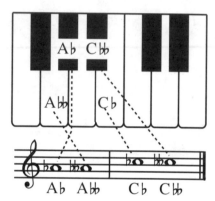

The **DOUBLE FLAT** lowers the **FLATTENED** note by a **CHROMATIC SEMITONE.** Flattened notes, which become double flat notes, are also played on the white keys, with the exception of C♭♭ and F♭♭, which are played on the black keys.

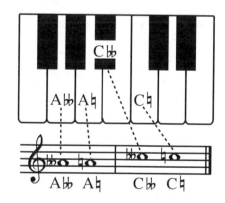

To cancel the double flat, raise the **DOUBLE FLAT NOTE TWO SEMITONES,** by using a **NATURAL SIGN.**

OR

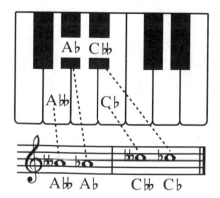

To cancel the double flat, raise the **DOUBLE FLAT** note by a **CHROMATIC SEMITONE,** by using a **FLAT SIGN.**

EXERCISES:

4. LOWER each note by a **WHOLE TONE**. Do **NOT** change the letternames.
Draw corresponding lines to the keyboard.

a.

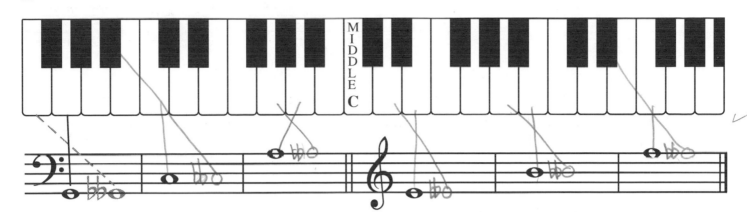

b. LOWER each note by a **CHROMATIC SEMITONE** and draw corresponding lines to the keyboard.

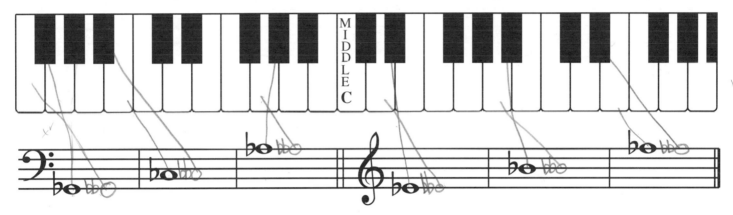

5. RAISE each note by a **WHOLE TONE.** Do **NOT** change the letternames.
Draw corresponding lines to the keyboard.

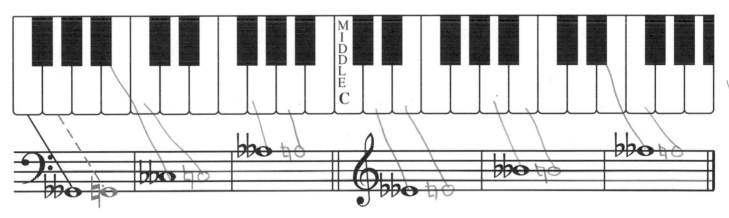

6. RAISE each **DOUBLE FLAT NOTE** by a **CHROMATIC SEMITONE** and draw
corresponding lines to the keyboard.

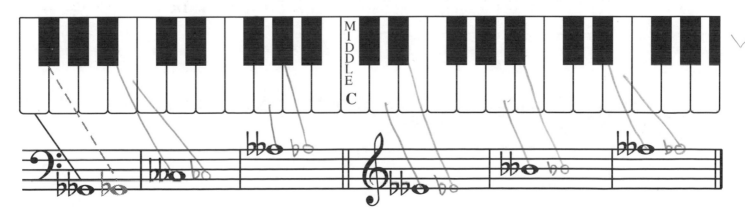

7. **RAISE** the notes by a **WHOLE TONE.** Do **NOT** change the letternames.

a.

b.

8. **RAISE** the notes by a **CHROMATIC SEMITONE.**

a.

b.

9. **LOWER** the notes by a **WHOLE TONE.** Do **NOT** change the letternames.

a.

b.

10. **LOWER** the notes by a **CHROMATIC SEMITONE.**

a.

b.

19

11. LOWER the notes by a **CHROMATIC SEMITONE.**

12. RAISE the notes by a **WHOLE TONE.** Do **NOT** change the letternames.

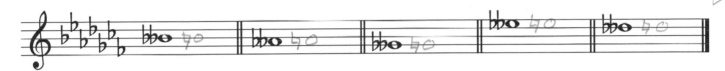

13. LOWER the notes by a **WHOLE TONE.** Do **NOT** change the letternames.

14. RAISE the notes by a **CHROMATIC SEMITONE.**

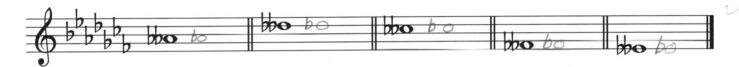

15. LOWER the notes by a **CHROMATIC SEMITONE.**

16. RAISE the notes by a **WHOLE TONE.** Use **DIFFERENT** letternames.

17. LOWER the notes by a **WHOLE TONE.** Use **DIFFERENT** letternames.

REVIEW No. 2

100

10

1. RAISE each note by a **WHOLE TONE.** Do **NOT** change the letternames.

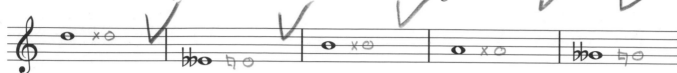

10

2. RAISE each note by a **CHROMATIC SEMITONE.**

10

3. Write the following scales ascending and descending, using a **KEY SIGNATURE.**

a.   C# Major, in quarter notes

b. *Raise 7*   g minor, harmonic form, in half notes

Raise 6+7 ↑ Lower 6+7↓

c.   f# minor, melodic form, in eighth notes.

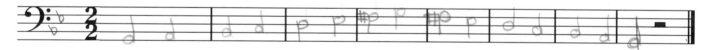

10

4. Add **RESTS** below each bracket to complete the measures.

10

5. Add **BAR LINES.**

Symphony in B minor

Allegretto moderato   Schubert

10 **6. LOWER** the notes by a **WHOLE TONE.** Do **NOT** change the letternames.

10 **7. LOWER** the notes by a **CHROMATIC SEMITONE.**

20 **8.** Write the **DOMINANT TRIAD** of each minor key.

Redo   April 5/2000

a.

b.

10 **9.** Allegro   Gurlitt

A

mf

B

C   D

✳ Put time sign in Both cleffs

ANALYSE the above excerpt and answer the following:

a. Name the **KEY.** D+ ✔

b. Name the **COMPOSER.** GURLITT ✔

c. Add the missing **TIME SIGNATURE** on the excerpt. 2/4 or 4/8

d. Give the meaning of the **TERMS** and **SIGNS** at the following letters on the excerpt:

? A. Allegro - fast (quick + lively)   B. mf = moderately loud (A little softer than f)?

C. c - STACATTO ✔   D. 𝇇 = ___ - hold for full value

e. **LABEL** and **CIRCLE** each of the following:

✔E. The scale of **D MAJOR.**   ✔F. The scale of **A MAJOR.**

✔G. Three **MAJOR 3RD** intervals.   ✔H. Three **QUARTER** rests.

✔I. Two **EIGHTH** rests.   Ⓙ One **SIXTEENTH** rest.

LESSON No. 3

Minor Scales

To identify the **KEY SIGNATURE** of a minor key, **GO UP 3 SEMITONES** from the tonic note to the **RELATIVE MAJOR KEY** and share its key signature.

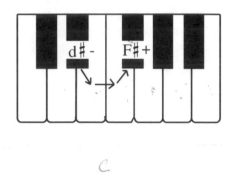

C

1. **3 SEMITONES ABOVE** the tonic note of d♯ minor is the **RELATIVE MAJOR, F♯ Major.**
   When naming the relative Major key, **ALWAYS SKIP** one alphabetical lettername: D - E̶ - F.
   As per example, the relative Major for d♯ minor is F♯ Major (not G♭ Major).
2. **F♯ Major** has six sharps: **F♯, C♯, G♯, D♯, A♯** and **E♯.**
3. **d♯ minor** shares the **F♯ Major** key signature
   Therefore, **d♯ minor** also has **F♯, C♯, G♯, D♯, A♯** and **E♯** in its key signature.

EXERCISES:

1. Find the **RELATIVE MAJOR KEY** for each of the **MINOR KEYS** shown on the keyboards. Name the **SHARPS** of the key signature shared by both keys.

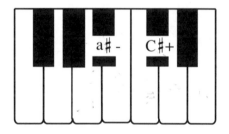

The **RELATIVE MAJOR** of a♯ minor is <u>C♯</u> Major

<u>C♯</u> **MAJOR** has 7 sharps: <u>F♯ C♯ G♯ D♯ A♯ E♯ B♯</u>

Therefore a♯ minor also has <u>F♯ C♯ G♯ D♯ A♯ E♯ B♯</u>

F   F♯

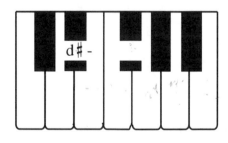

The **RELATIVE MAJOR** of d♯ minor is <u>F♯ +</u>

<u>F♯</u> **MAJOR** has <u>6</u> sharps: <u>F C G D A E</u>

Therefore d♯ minor also has <u>F C G D A E</u>   6 sharps ✓

YES
Do I have to put the sharps in on just the letter Names since sharps is already mentioned

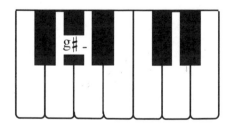

The **RELATIVE MAJOR** of g♯ minor is <u>B +</u>

<u>B</u> **MAJOR** has <u>5</u> sharps: <u>F C G D A</u>

Therefore g♯ minor also has <u>5 sharps   F C G D A</u> ✓

2. Fill in the blanks.

MINOR KEY	RELATIVE MAJOR KEY	KEY SIGNATURE
e minor	G +	F#
b minor	D +	F# C#
f♯ minor	A +	F# C# G#
c♯ minor	E +	F# C# G D#
g♯ minor	B +	F# C# G# D# A#
d♯ minor	F# +	F# C# G D# A# E#
a♯ minor	C# +	F# C# G# D A# E# B#

✓

3. The **RELATIVE MINOR KEY** of:

C♯ Major is __A# -__ ✓; B Major is __G# -__ ✓; A Major i s __F# -__ ✓; G Major is __E -__ ✓

F♯ Major is __D# -__ ✓; E Major is __C# -__ ✓; D Major is __B -__ ✓; C Major is __A -__ ✓

4. Name the **MAJOR** and **MINOR KEY** for each key signature.

a.

Major: __C# +__ ✓ · · · __B +__ ✓ · · · __A +__ ✓ · · · __G +__ ✓

minor: __A# -__ ✓ · · · __G# -__ ✓ · · · __F# -__ ✓ · · · __E -__ ✓

b.

Major: __C +__ ✓ · · · __E +__ ✓ · · · __D +__ ✓ · · · __F# +__ ✓

minor: __A -__ · · · __C# -__ ✓ · · · __B -__ ✓ · · · __d# -__ ✓

5. Write the **KEY SIGNATURE**, for each of the minor keys below.

F C G A C B

a.

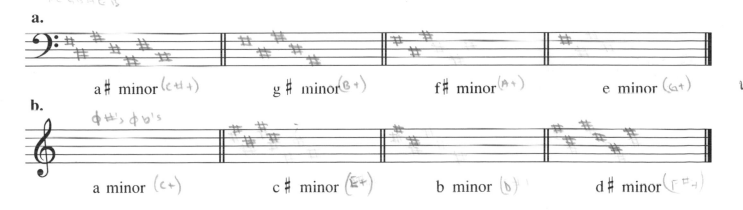

a♯ minor (c#+) · · · g♯ minor (B+) · · · f♯ minor (A+) · · · e minor (G+) ✓

b.

♯#'s, ♯b's

a minor (C+) · · · c♯ minor (E+) · · · b minor (D) · · · d♯ minor (F#+)

Remember, to identify the **KEY SIGNATURE** of a minor key, **GO UP 3 SEMITONES** from the tonic note to the **RELATIVE MAJOR KEY** and share its key signature.

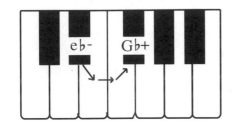

1. **3 SEMITONES ABOVE** the tonic note of e♭ minor is the **RELATIVE MAJOR, G♭ Major.**
   When naming the relative Major key, **ALWAYS SKIP** one alphabetical lettername: E - F̶ - G .
   As per example, the relative Major for e♭ minor is G♭ Major (not F♯ Major).

2. **G♭ Major** has six flats: **B♭, E♭, A♭, D♭, G♭** and **C♭.**

3. e♭ **minor** shares the **G♭ Major** key signature.
   Therefore e♭ **minor** also has **B♭, E♭, A♭, D♭, G♭** and **C♭** in its key signature.

EXERCISES:

6. Find the **RELATIVE MAJOR KEY** for each of the **MINOR KEYS** shown on the keyboards. Name the **FLATS** of the key signature shared by both keys.

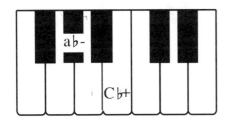

The **RELATIVE MAJOR** of a♭ minor is C♭ Major

C♭ **MAJOR** has 7 flats: B♭ E♭ A♭ D♭ G♭ C♭ F♭

Therefore a♭ minor also has B♭ E♭ A♭ D♭ G♭ C♭ F♭

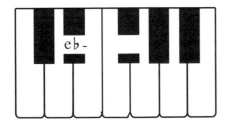

The **RELATIVE MAJOR** of e♭ minor is Gb+   ✓

Gb **MAJOR** has 6 flats: B E A D G C

Therefore e♭ minor also has 6 Flats BEADGC

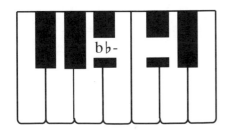

The **RELATIVE MAJOR** of b♭ minor is Db +   ✓

Db **MAJOR** has 5 flats: B E A D G

Therefore b♭ minor also has 5 Flats BEADG

7. Fill in the blanks.

MINOR KEY	RELATIVE MAJOR KEY	KEY SIGNATURES
a minor	C+	∅ Sharps Flats
d minor	F+	B♭
g minor	B♭+	B♭ E♭
c minor	E♭+	B♭ E♭ A♭
f minor	A♭+	B♭ E♭ A♭ D♭
b♭ minor	D♭+	B♭ E♭ A♭ D♭ G♭
e♭ minor	G♭+	B♭ E♭ A♭ D♭ G♭ C♭
a♭ minor	C♭+	B♭ E♭ A♭ D♭ G♭ C♭ F♭

8. Write the **RELATIVE MINOR KEY** of each of the following Major keys.

C♭ Major __A♭–__ ✓; D♭ Major __B♭–__ ✓; E♭ Major __c–__ ✓; F Major __D–__ ✓.

G♭ Major __E♭–__ ✓; A♭ Major __F–__ ✓; B♭ Major __G–__ ✓; C Major __A–__ ✓.

9. Name the **MAJOR** and **MINOR** key of each key signature.

a.

Major: __C♭+__   __D♭+__ ✓   __E♭+__ ✓   __F+__ ✓

minor: __A♭–__ ✓   __B♭–__   __c–__   __D–__

b.

Major: __C+__   __A♭+__   __B♭+__ ✓   __G♭+__

minor: __A–__ ✓   __F–__ ✓   __G–__ ✓   __E♭–__ ✓

10. Write the **KEY SIGNATURE,** for each of the minor keys below.

a.

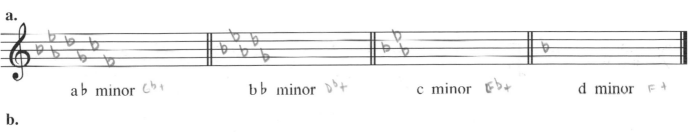

a♭ minor C♭+   b♭ minor D♭+   c minor E♭+   d minor F+ ✓

b.

a minor C+   f minor A♭+   g minor B♭+   e♭ minor G♭+

The Minor Scale, Harmonic Form

EXAMPLE:

Remember, when writing a **HARMONIC MINOR SCALE,** always write the **NATURAL MINOR SCALE** first.

d♯ natural minor, using a key signature:

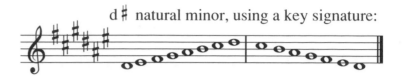

Then **RAISE** the 7th note by a Chromatic Semitone (C♯ becomes C𝄪) Notice how a **BAR LINE** cancels all accidentals and C𝄪 is repeated.

d♯ harmonic minor, using a key signature:

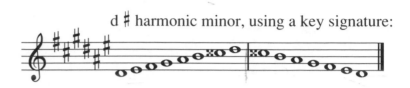

EXERCISES:

11. Write the following scales ascending and descending in eighth notes, using a **KEY SIGNATURE.**

a. (F♯ +)   d♯ minor, natural form

b. (C♯ +)   a♯ minor, natural form

c. B+   g♯ minor, natural form

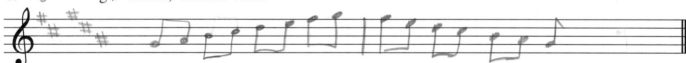

12. Write the following scales ascending and descending, using a **KEY SIGNATURE.**

a. (C♯ +)   a♯ minor, harmonic form (in the bass clef)

b. B♭   g♯ minor, harmonic form (in the bass clef)

c.   d♯ minor, harmonic form (in the treble clef)

EXAMPLE:

In the **NATURAL MINOR SCALE** the **SEMITONES** are always found between the notes **2 - 3** and **5 - 6**.

g♯ natural minor, using accidentals:

In the **HARMONIC MINOR SCALE** the **SEMITONES** are always found between **2 - 3**, **5 - 6** and **7 - 8**. Notice how **F♯** becomes **F×** .

g♯ harmonic minor, using accidentals:

EXERCISES:

13. Add **ACCIDENTALS** and mark the **SEMITONES** with a slur.

a.   g♯ minor, natural form

b.   d♯ minor, natural form

c.   a♯ minor, natural form

14. Write the following scales ascending and descending in whole notes, using **ACCIDENTALS.** Mark the **SEMITONES** with a slur.

a.   d♯ minor, harmonic form

b.   g♯ minor, harmonic form

c.   a♯ minor, harmonic form

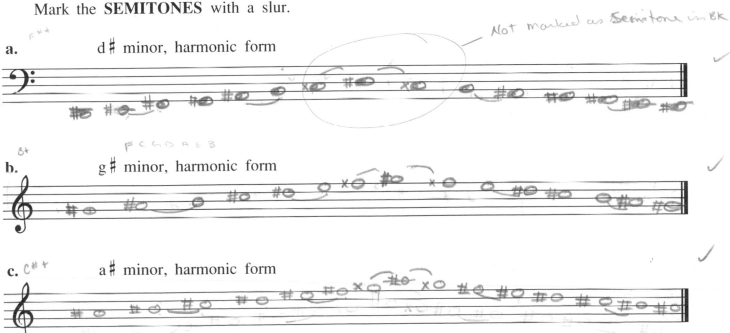

EXAMPLE:

Remember, when writing a **HARMONIC MINOR SCALE,** always write the **NATURAL MINOR SCALE** first.

e♭ natural minor, using a key signature:

Then **RAISE** the 7th note by a Chromatic Semitone. (**D♭** becomes **D♮**)

e♭ harmonic minor, using a key signature:

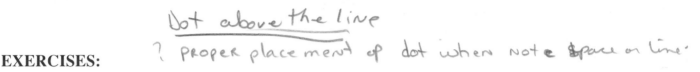

Dot above the line
? PROPER placement of dot when note space on line.

EXERCISES:

15. Write the following scales in dotted half notes, using a **KEY SIGNATURE.**

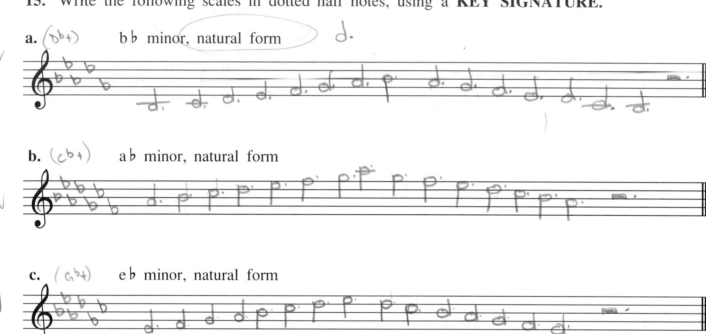

a. (D♭+)   b♭ minor, natural form

b. (C♭+)   a♭ minor, natural form

c. (G♭+)   e♭ minor, natural form

16. Write the following scales in quarter notes, using a **KEY SIGNATURE.**

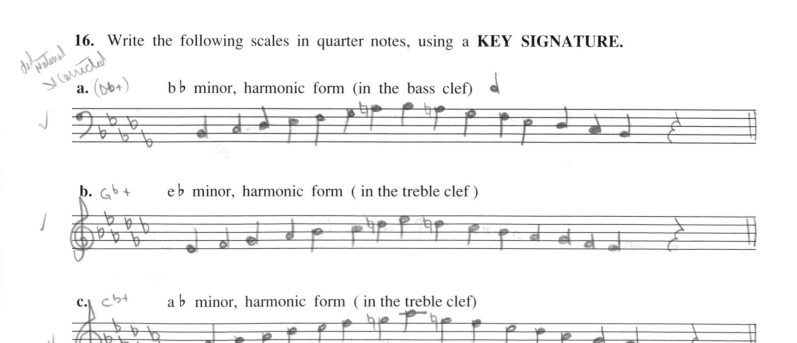

a. (D♭+)   b♭ minor, harmonic form (in the bass clef)

b. G♭+   e♭ minor, harmonic form (in the treble clef)

c. C♭+   a♭ minor, harmonic form (in the treble clef)

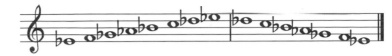

EXAMPLE:

In the e♭ minor scale there are six flats:
B♭, E♭, A♭, D♭, G♭ and C♭.
The **7th NOTE** of the scale is **D♭**.

e♭ natural minor, using accidentals:

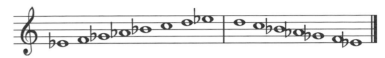

In scales written without a key signature, the 7th note in the minor harmonic form is **RAISED** by leaving out the accidental. (D♭ becomes **D**, not **D♮**)

e♭ harmonic minor, using accidentals:

EXERCISES:

Nat   2-3
       5-6

Har   2-3
       5-6
       7-8

17. Add **ACCIDENTALS** and mark the **SEMITONES** with a slur.

a. (C♭+) BEADGCF   a♭ minor, natural form

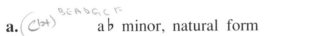

b. (G♭+) BEADGC   e♭ minor, natural form

c. (D♭+) BEADG   b♭ minor, natural form

18. Write the following scales in half notes, using **ACCIDENTALS**.
Mark the **SEMITONES** with a slur.

a. (C♭+)   a♭ minor, harmonic form

b. BEADG D♭+   b♭ minor, harmonic form

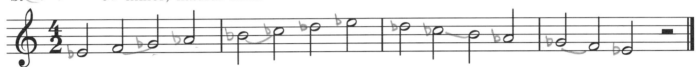

c. BEADGC G♭+   e♭ minor, harmonic form

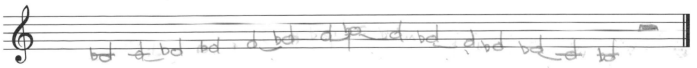
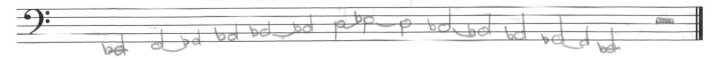

The Minor Scale, Melodic Form

EXAMPLE:

Remember, when writing a **MELODIC MINOR SCALE**, always write the **NATURAL MINOR SCALE** first.

a♯ natural minor, using a key signature:

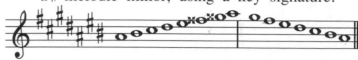

Then **RAISE** the 6th and 7th notes by a **CHROMATIC SEMITONE** ascending only. (F♯ becomes F×; G♯ becomes G×)

a♯ melodic minor, using a key signature:

EXERCISES: WRITE IN CORRECTION (omit Bar line) NOT IN exams.

19. Change each natural minor scale into a **MELODIC MINOR SCALE.**

a. d♯ minor

b. g♯ minor

c. a♯ minor

20. Write the following scales in sixteenth notes, using a **KEY SIGNATURE.**

a. (B+) g♯ minor, melodic form (in the bass clef)

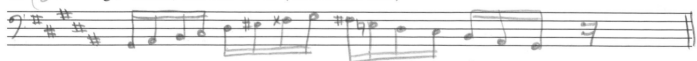

b. c♯+ a♯ minor, melodic form (in the bass clef)

c. f× d♯ minor, melodic form (in the treble clef)

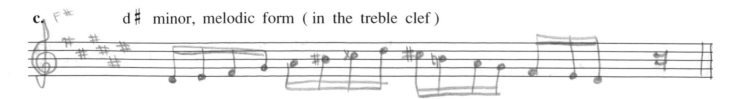

EXAMPLE:

In the **NATURAL MINOR SCALE**, the **SEMITONES** are always found between the notes **2 - 3** and **5 - 6**.

g# natural minor, using accidentals:

In the **MELODIC MINOR SCALE,** the **SEMITONES** are always found between the notes **2 - 3** and **7 - 8** (ascending) and between the notes **2 - 3** and **5 - 6** (descending).

g# melodic minor, using accidentals:

EXERCISES:

21. Add **ACCIDENTALS** and mark the **SEMITONES** with a slur.

a. a# minor, natural form

b. g# minor, natural form

c. d# minor, natural form

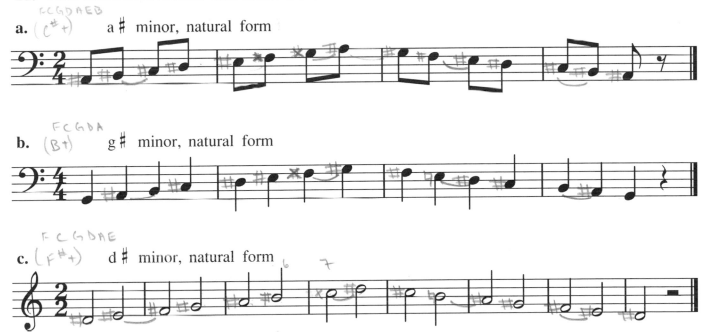

22. Write the following scales in whole notes, using **ACCIDENTALS.**
Mark the **SEMITONES** with a slur.

a. d# minor, melodic form (in the bass clef)

b. a# minor, melodic form (in the treble clef)

c. g# minor, melodic form (in the treble clef)

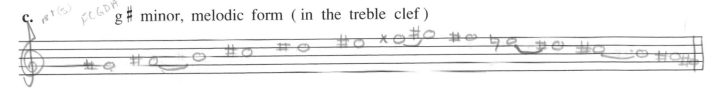

EXAMPLE:

Remember, when writing a **MELODIC MINOR SCALE**, always write the **NATURAL MINOR SCALE** first.

ab natural minor, using a key signature:

Then **RAISE** the **6th** and **7th** notes ascending only, by a **CHROMATIC SEMITONE**.

ab melodic minor, using a key signature:

EXERCISES:

23. Write the following scales in dotted half notes, using a **KEY SIGNATURE.**

a. bb minor, natural form

b. eb minor, natural form

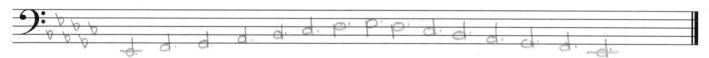

c. ab minor, natural form

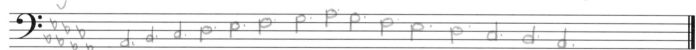

24. Write the following scales in quarter notes, using a **KEY SIGNATURE.**

a. bb minor, melodic form (in the bass clef)

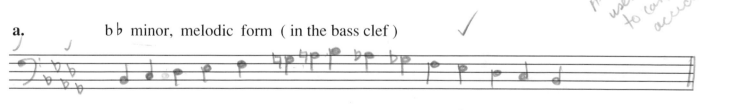

b. eb minor, melodic form (in the treble clef)

c. ab minor, melodic form (in the treble clef)

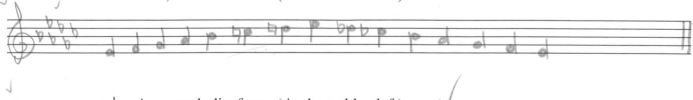

EXAMPLE:

When flats affect the **6th** and **7th** notes, of a scale written with accidentals, these notes are **RAISED** a **CHROMATIC SEMITONE** by leaving out the accidentals.

Do **NOT** use natural signs.
(**F♭** becomes **F** and **G♭** becomes **G**)

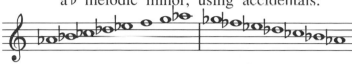

a♭ natural minor, using accidentals:

a♭ melodic minor, using accidentals:

EXERCISES:

25. Add **ACCIDENTALS** and mark the **SEMITONES** with a slur.

a.   a♭ minor, melodic form

b.   e♭ minor, melodic form

c.   b♭ minor, melodic form

26. Write the following scales in half notes, using **ACCIDENTALS.**
Mark the **SEMITONES** with a slur.

a.   a♭ minor, melodic form

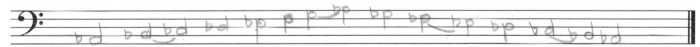

b.   b♭ minor, melodic form

c.   e♭ minor, melodic form

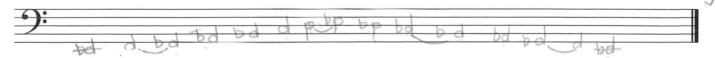

EXAMPLES:

Handwritten annotations: TONIC C — C min / C maj. Tonic shares the same TONIC I note. Relative shares Key signiture.

C Major:

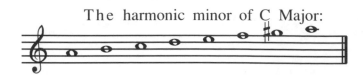

C Major has **NO SHARPS** or **FLATS.**

The harmonic minor of C Major:

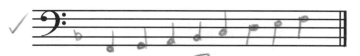

The **RELATIVE MINOR** of C Major is a minor. (Count 3 semitones down: C - B - A)

The tonic minor of C Major (melodic):

The **TONIC** note of C Major is **C.** Therefore the **TONIC MINOR** of C Major is c minor.

27. Write the following scales in quarter notes, **ASCENDING** only.

USING A KEY SIGNATURE	**USING ACCIDENTALS**

a.   F Major

g.   G Major

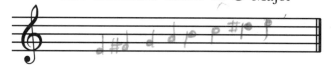

b.   The harmonic minor of F Major

h.   The harmonic minor of G Major

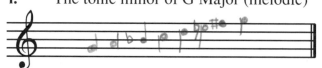

c.   The tonic minor of F Major (melodic)

i.   The tonic minor of G Major (melodic)

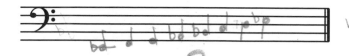

d.   D Major

j.   E♭ Major

e.   The harmonic minor of D Major

k.   The harmonic minor of E♭ Major

f.   The tonic minor of D Major (melodic)

l.   The tonic minor of E♭ Major (melodic)

Handwritten annotations: "Relative" and "R" markings throughout. "Don't need Natural Sign" at bottom right.

35

28. Write the following scales in eighth notes, **ASCENDING** only.

USING A KEY SIGNATURE	USING ACCIDENTALS

a. A Major

j. A♭ Major

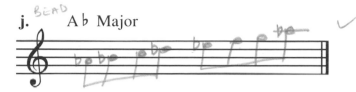

b. The harmonic minor of A Major

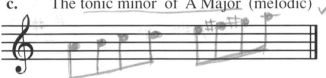

k. The harmonic minor of A♭ Major

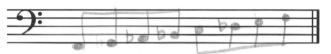

c. The tonic minor of A Major (melodic)

l. The tonic minor of A♭ Major (melodic)

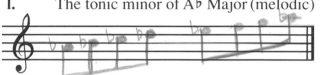

d. E Major

m. C♯ Major

e. The harmonic minor of E Major

n. The harmonic minor of C♯ Major

f. The tonic minor of E Major (melodic)

o. The tonic minor of C♯ Major (melodic)

g. F♯ Major

p. B Major

h. The harmonic minor of F♯ Major

q. The harmonic minor of B Major

i. The tonic minor of F♯ Major (melodic)

r. The tonic minor of B Major (melodic)

36
100

20   1. Write the following scales ascending and descending in half notes, using **ACCIDENTALS**.
     Circle and label the **DOMINANT NOTE** of each scale.

FCGDAEB
a.   C♯ Major   ↑↓ 7#'s ⌄

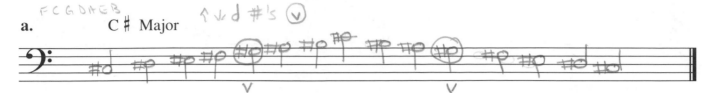

b.   A♯ -   the relative minor of C♯ Major (natural form)

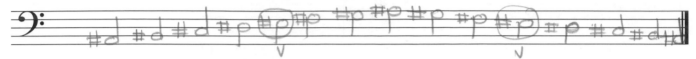

c.   the relative minor of C♯ Major (harmonic form)

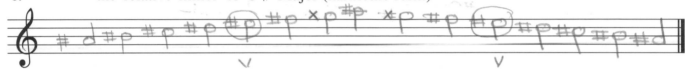

d.   the tonic minor of C♯ Major (melodic form)

10   2. Add **RESTS** below each bracket to complete the measures.

a.

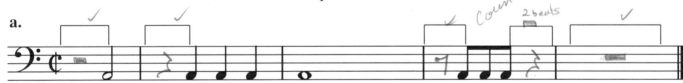

b

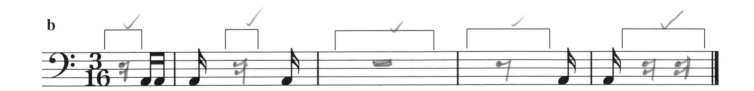

10   3. Add a **TIME SIGNATURE** to the beginning of each measure.

10 **4.** Raise the notes by a **WHOLE TONE**, using the **SAME** letternames.

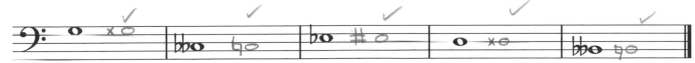

10 **5.** Raise the notes by a **WHOLE TONE**, using **DIFFERENT** letternames.

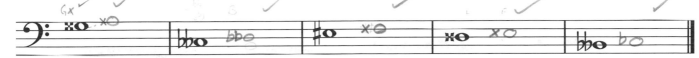

10 **6.** Change each note **ENHARMONICALLY.**

10 **7.** Circle the notes that do **NOT** belong to the key. **NAME** the harmonic intervals.

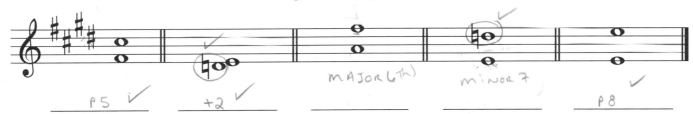

MAJOR (6TH)   MINOR 7

P 5 ✓   +2 ✓   ___   ___   P 8

A BCDEFGABCD   1 0

20 **8.** (i) Name the **KEY** of the following melody.

(ii) Write the corresponding scale, using a **KEY SIGNATURE** and name the **KEY.**

Valse Op. 69 No. 2

(i)   **Moderato**   **Chopin**

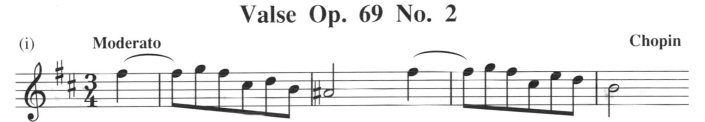

Key: B minor ✓

(ii)

Key: B minor HARMONIC ✓

LESSON No. 4

Technical Degree Names for the Notes of the Scale

The **ROMAN NUMERALS** and **TECHNICAL DEGREES** for Major scales are as follows:

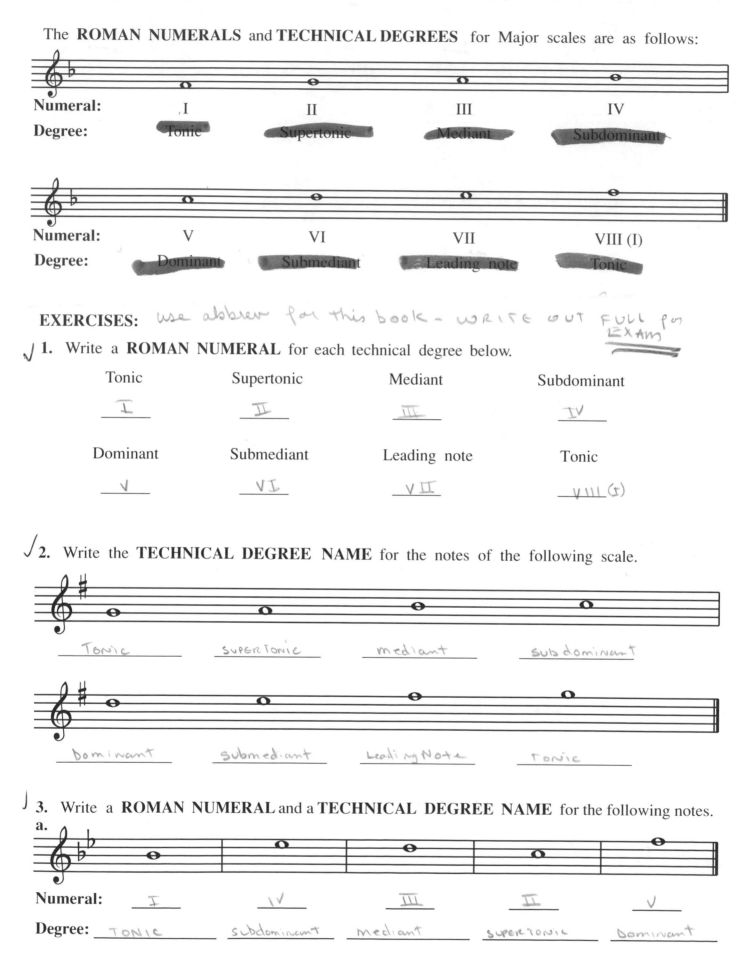

Numeral:	I	II	III	IV
Degree:	Tonic	Supertonic	Mediant	Subdominant

Numeral:	V	VI	VII	VIII (I)
Degree:	Dominant	Submediant	Leading note	Tonic

EXERCISES: *use abbrev for this book – WRITE OUT FULL for EXAM*

✓ **1.** Write a **ROMAN NUMERAL** for each technical degree below.

Tonic	Supertonic	Mediant	Subdominant
I	II	III	IV

Dominant	Submediant	Leading note	Tonic
V	VI	VII	VIII (I)

✓ **2.** Write the **TECHNICAL DEGREE NAME** for the notes of the following scale.

Tonic   SuperTonic   mediant   subdominant

Dominant   Submediant   Leading Note   Tonic

✓ **3.** Write a **ROMAN NUMERAL** and a **TECHNICAL DEGREE NAME** for the following notes.

a.

Numeral:	I	IV	III	II	V
Degree:	TONIC	Subdominant	mediant	superTonic	Dominant

b.

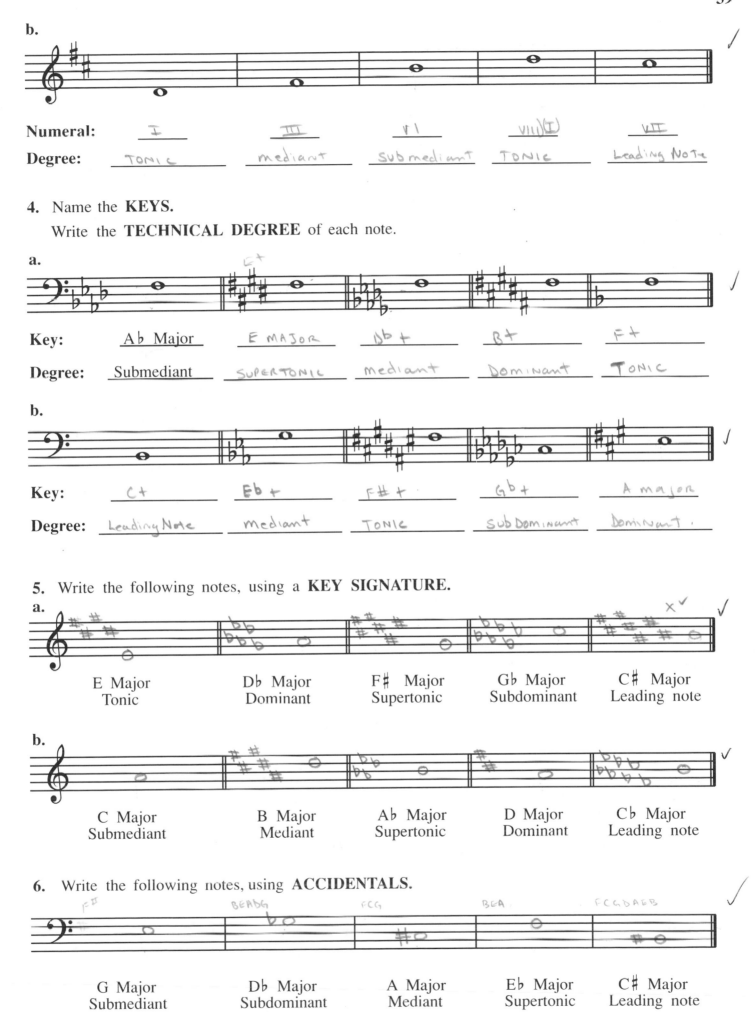

Numeral: _I_ _III_ _VI_ _VIII(I)_ _VII_
Degree: _TONIC_ _mediant_ _submediant_ _TONIC_ _Leading Note_

4. Name the **KEYS.**

Write the **TECHNICAL DEGREE** of each note.

a.

Key: _Ab Major_ _E MAJOR_ _Db +_ _B+_ _F+_
Degree: _Submediant_ _SUPERTONIC_ _mediant_ _Dominant_ _TONIC_

b.

Key: _C+_ _Eb +_ _F# +_ _Gb +_ _A major_
Degree: _Leading Note_ _mediant_ _TONIC_ _Subdominant_ _Dominant._

5. Write the following notes, using a **KEY SIGNATURE.**

a.

E Major — Tonic   Db Major — Dominant   F# Major — Supertonic   Gb Major — Subdominant   C# Major — Leading note

b.

C Major — Submediant   B Major — Mediant   Ab Major — Supertonic   D Major — Dominant   Cb Major — Leading note

6. Write the following notes, using **ACCIDENTALS.**

G Major — Submediant   Db Major — Subdominant   A Major — Mediant   Eb Major — Supertonic   C# Major — Leading note

EXAMPLE:

The **TECHNICAL DEGREE NAMES** for the notes of the **HARMONIC** minor scale are the **SAME** as for the notes of the Major scale. Remember that the 7th note is raised by a c. s.

Numeral:	I	II	III	IV
Degree:	Tonic	Supertonic	Mediant	Subdominant

Numeral:	V	VI	VII	VIII (I)
Degree:	Dominant	Submediant	Leading note	Tonic

EXERCISES:

x ✔   Read Scale

7. Write **ROMAN NUMERALS** and **TECHNICAL DEGREE NAMES** for the following minor scale.

Gm

Numeral:	I	II	VIII(I)	IV
Degree:	TONIC	SUPERTONIC	mediant	subdominant

Numeral:	IV	VI	VII	VIII (I)
Degree:	Dominant	submediant	Leading Not	TONIC

Look @ Whole Scale to Determine Key

8. Write a **ROMAN NUMERAL** and a **TECHNICAL DEGREE NAME** for the notes below.

a.

Key:	D - harm			
Numeral:	I	V	VI	VII	VIII(I)
Degree:	Tonic	Dominant	Submediant	Leading Note	TONIC

b.

Key:	E - Harm			
Numeral:	I	VI	VII	II	IV
Degree:	Tonic	Submediant	Leading Note	SUPERTONIC	Subdominant

EXAMPLE:

Notice how all the **LEADING NOTES** are raised in the minor scale.

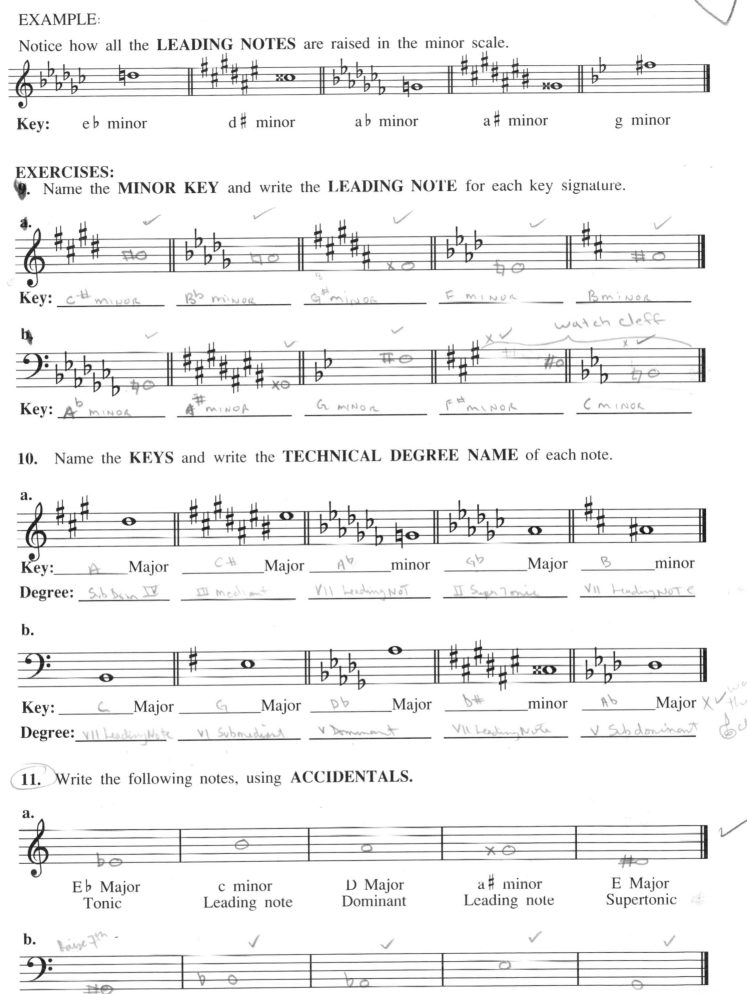

Key: e♭ minor   d♯ minor   a♭ minor   a♯ minor   g minor

EXERCISES:

9. Name the **MINOR KEY** and write the **LEADING NOTE** for each key signature.

a.

Key: C♯ minor   B♭ minor   G♯ minor   F minor   B minor

b.

Key: A♭ minor   A♯ minor   G minor   F♯ minor   C minor

10. Name the **KEYS** and write the **TECHNICAL DEGREE NAME** of each note.

a.

Key: _A_ Major   _C♯_ Major   _A♭_ minor   _G♭_ Major   _B_ minor

Degree: Sub Dom IV   III mediant   VII Leading NOT   II Super Tonic   VII Leading NOTE

b.

Key: _C_ Major   _G_ Major   _D♭_ Major   _D♯_ minor   _A♭_ Major

Degree: VII Leading Note   VI Submediant   V Dominant   VII Leading Note   V Subdominant

11. Write the following notes, using **ACCIDENTALS.**

a.

E♭ Major   c minor   D Major   a♯ minor   E Major
Tonic   Leading note   Dominant   Leading note   Supertonic

b. raise 7th –

a minor   F Major   f minor   G Major   a♭ minor
Leading note Subdominant   Mediant   Submediant   Leading note
(C♯)   (A♭♮)   (C♭♮)

EXAMPLE:

The **TECHNICAL DEGREE NAMES** for the notes of the **MELODIC** minor scale are the **SAME** as for the notes of the Major and harmonic minor scales. Remember that the 6th and 7th notes are raised by a chromatic semitone in melodic minor scales, ascending only.

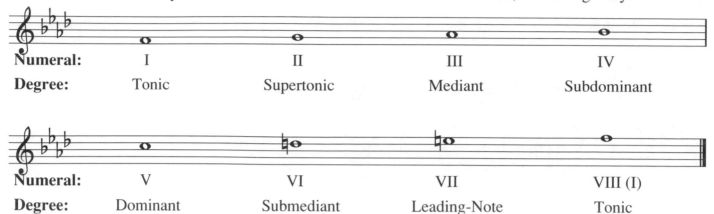

Numeral:	I	II	III	IV
Degree:	Tonic	Supertonic	Mediant	Subdominant

Numeral:	V	VI	VII	VIII (I)
Degree:	Dominant	Submediant	Leading-Note	Tonic

EXERCISES:

12. Write **ROMAN NUMERALS** and **TECHNICAL DEGREE NAMES** for the minor scale below.

G minor

Numeral:	I	II	III	IV
Degree:	Tonic	Supertonic	mediant	Subdominant

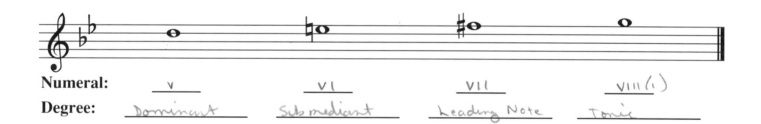

Numeral:	V	VI	VII	VIII (I)
Degree:	Dominant	Sub mediant	Leading Note	Tonic

EXAMPLE:

Notice how the 6th and 7th notes are raised in the **MELODIC** minor scale.

EXERCISES:

13. Name the **MINOR** key and write a **SUBMEDIANT** note for each key signature.

a.

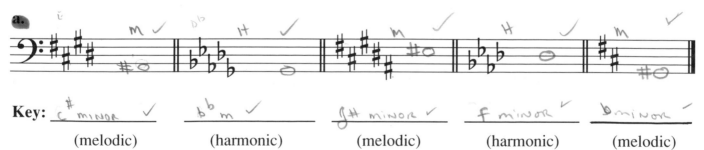

Key:	c# minor	bb m	g# minor	f minor	b minor
	(melodic)	(harmonic)	(melodic)	(harmonic)	(melodic)

b.

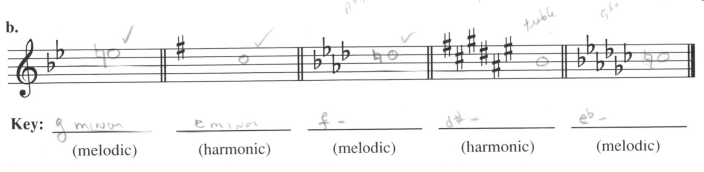

Key: _g minor_   _e minor_   _f –_   _d# –_   _eb –_
(melodic)   (harmonic)   (melodic)   (harmonic)   (melodic)

14. Name the **KEYS** and write the **TECHNICAL DEGREE NAME** of each note.

a.

Key: _a_ minor   _G_ Major   _d_ minor   _C_ Major   _g_ minor
Degree: _Tonic_   _mediant_   _supertonic_   _Submediant_   _Leading Note_

b.

Key: _Db_ Major   _f#_ minor   _Eb_ Major   _D#_ minor   _Cb_ Major
Degree: _Dominant_   _Leading Note_   _Tonic_   _submediant_   _Leading Note_

c.

Key: _a#_ minor   _D_ Major   _eb_ minor   _B_ Major   _bb_ minor
Degree: _Leading Note_   _IV Subdominant_   _6th Submediant_   _6th Submediant_   _6th Submediant_

15. Write the following notes, using **ACCIDENTALS** where necessary.

a.

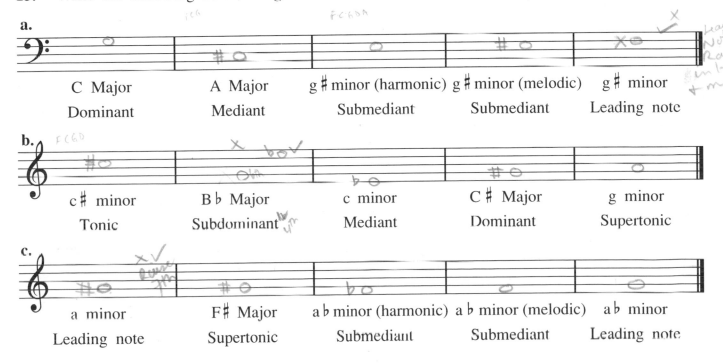

C Major   A Major   g# minor (harmonic)   g# minor (melodic)   g# minor
Dominant   Mediant   Submediant   Submediant   Leading note

b.

c# minor   Bb Major   c minor   C# Major   g minor
Tonic   Subdominant   Mediant   Dominant   Supertonic

c.

a minor   F# Major   ab minor (harmonic)   ab minor (melodic)   ab minor
Leading note   Supertonic   Submediant   Submediant   Leading note

16. Write the following scales ascending and descending in quarter notes, using a **KEY SIGNATURE**.
Begin each scale on the **TONIC** note.

a. the Major scale with G as its dominant note

b. the minor scale, harmonic form, with F♯ as its supertonic note

G⁺
F♯ as 2nd
II
E minor

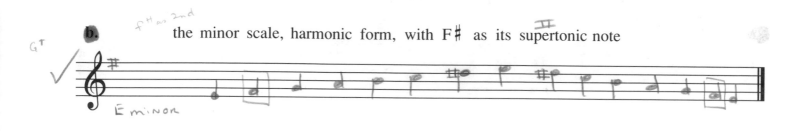

c. the Major scale with C♯ as its submediant note

E⁺
VI

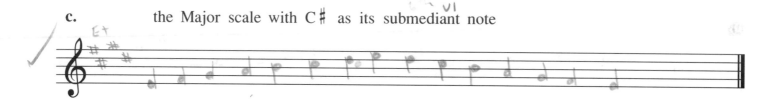

d. the minor scale, melodic form, with B♭ as its mediant note

G⁻
III

BEADGCF   ABCDEFGA

e. the Major scale with D♭ as its subdominant note

IV

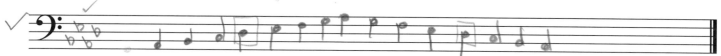

A'BC'D'EFG'A'BC'D'EF
FCGDAEB'C♯   D♭⁻   4 sharps
C♯ – Relative + = E
(Key sg X)
VII
Raised 7
B Natural

f. the minor scale, harmonic form, with B♯ as its leading note

C♯ minor

FCGDAE

g. the Major scale with F♯ as its mediant note

D

17. Write the following scales ascending and descending in eighth notes, using **ACCIDENTALS**. Begin each scale on the **TONIC** note.

a. the minor scale, melodic form, with E♭ as its tonic note

b. the minor scale, harmonic form, with D♯ as its dominant note

c. the Major scale with B♭ as its subdominant note

d. the minor scale, melodic form, with B♯ as its submediant note

e. the minor scale, harmonic form, with G as its leading note

f. the Major scale with A♯ as its mediant note

g. the minor scale, melodic form, with G as its supertonic note

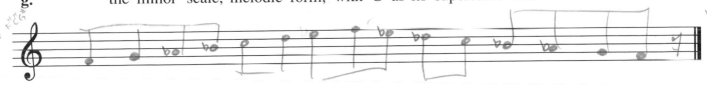

REVIEW No. 4

100

10

1. Name the **KEY** of each of the following key signatures.

   Write the **TECHNICAL DEGREE NAME** of each note.

Key: _____G_____ Major _____Db_____ Major _____A_____ Major _____f_____ minor _____g#_____ minor

Degree: ³ mediant   IV SUB dominant   v Dominant   6 sub mediant   7ᵗʰ Leading Note

20

2. Write the following scales ascending and descending in whole notes, using a **KEY SIGNATURE.**

   Begin each scale on the **TONIC** note.

   a. FCGDAE   the Major scale with D♯ as its supertonic

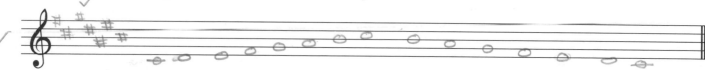

   b. the minor scale, harmonic form, with F as its dominant

   c. the minor scale, natural form, with G as its subdominant

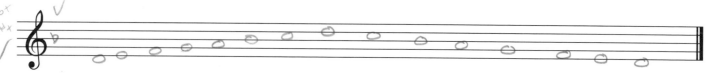

   d. the minor scale, melodic form, with A as its submediant

10

3. Write **RESTS** below each bracket to complete the measures.

had 4 quarters

10

4. Add **BAR LINES**

FCGDAEB
A#-   c#+ 7 #'s

10 **5.** Write the following notes, using **ACCIDENTALS.**

BEADG

BEAD

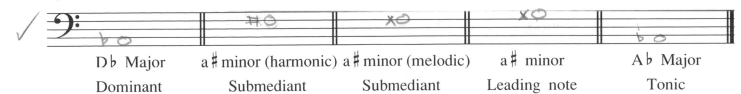

Db Major	a♯ minor (harmonic)	a♯ minor (melodic)	a♯ minor	Ab Major
Dominant	Submediant	Submediant	Leading note	Tonic

10 **6. RAISE** the notes by a **WHOLE TONE.** Do **NOT** change the lettername.

Natural signs needed

30 **7.**

Fantasia

G.P. Telemann

ANALYSE the above excerpt and answer the following:

a. Name the **COMPOSER.** GP Telemann   b. Name the **TITLE.** Fantasia .

c. Add the missing **TIME SIGNATURE** on the excerpt. 3/4

d. Name the **KEY.** Bb+   e. Number the **MEASURES** on the excerpt. (4)

f. Which measures have the same **SEQUENCES** in the treble and bass clefs?

Measures 1 and 2 .

Find the following at the **LETTERS** marked on the excerpt.

g. Name the **MELODIC** intervals at the following letters:

A -2nd ; B P4 ; C +2 ; D +6 ; E -7 .

h. Give the meaning of the **TERMS** and **SIGNS** at the following letters:

F allegro - fast   G mf moderately loud

H staccato - meaning detached   I slur mark - all notes to be played smoothly + joined (connected)

i. Is the triad at the letter J - **MAJOR** or **MINOR**? + ;

- **TONIC** or **DOMINANT**? Dom .

LESSON No. 5

Rewriting Major Key Melodies, Using a Key Signature

When writing a melody with a **KEY SIGNATURE** instead of accidentals:

1. Gather all the accidentals found in a Major melody and group them in the correct order:
    B♭, E♭, A♭, D♭, G♭, C♭, F♭ or F♯, C♯, G♯, D♯, A♯, E♯, B♯.

2. If the sharps or flats appear in the correct order, the melody is in a Major key.

3. To name the key, look at the **LAST NOTE** of the melody. It often ends on a **TONIC NOTE**.

Ecossaise in A flat Major

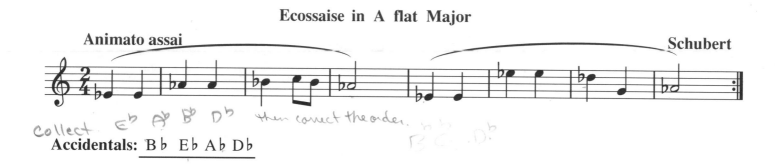

Collect   E♭ A♭ B♭ D♭   then correct the order.   B♭ C ♭ D♭

Accidentals: B♭ E♭ A♭ D♭

4. When rewriting melodies, using a **KEY SIGNATURE**, be sure to add all markings
    (e.g. slurs, dynamics, composer etc.).
    Remember, the **KEY SIGNATURE** is placed **BETWEEN** the clef and the time signature.

Ecossaise in A flat Major

Key: A♭ Major

Key: A♭ Major

EXERCISES:

1. (i) **PLAY** the following melodies and name the **ACCIDENTALS.**

(ii) **REWRITE** each melody, using a **KEY SIGNATURE** and name the **KEY.**

(iii) Write the corresponding scale, ascending and descending, using a **KEY SIGNATURE** and name the **KEY.**

a. (i) **Andante**   **Verdi**

Accidentals: B♭ E♭ A♭ D♭ G♭

(ii)

Key: D♭ +

(iii)

Key: D♭ +

b. (i) **Moderato**   **Mexico**

Collect. G♯ F♯ C♯

Accidentals: F♯ C♯ G♯   A♯

(ii)

Key: A +

(iii)

Key: A +

50

c. (i) **Vivace**   **United States**

Accidentals: ___F#___

(ii) Vivace   UNITED STATES

Key: ___G+___

(iii)

Key: ___G+___

d. (i)   **Germany**

Accidentals: ___Eb Ab Bb Bb___

(ii)   GERMANY

Key: ___Ab+___

(iii)

Key: ___Ab+___

Be careful, the following two melodies do **NOT** end on the **TONIC NOTE.**

Piano Sonata No. 4

e. (i) **Allegro**   L. van Beethoven

p dolce

Accidentals: Bb Eb Ab   Eb♮

(ii)

PIANO SONATA NO. 4

Allegro

L. van Beethoven

p dolce

Key: Eb+

(iii)

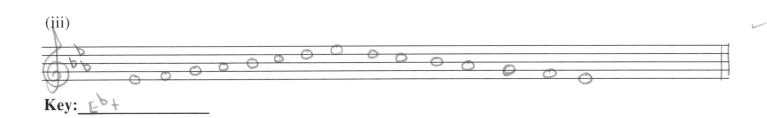

Key: Eb+

f. (i) **Moderato**   **Ireland**

Accidentals: F# C# G# D# A# E# B#

(ii)

MODERATO

IRELAND

Key: C#+

(iii)

Key: C#+

The following melodies are in the **MAJOR KEY** and do end on the **TONIC NOTE.**

Be careful, some of the **SHARPS** or **FLATS** are **MISSING.**

2. (i) **PLAY** the following melodies and name the **ACCIDENTALS.**

(ii) Rewrite each melody, using a **KEY SIGNATURE** and name the **KEY.**

a. (i)

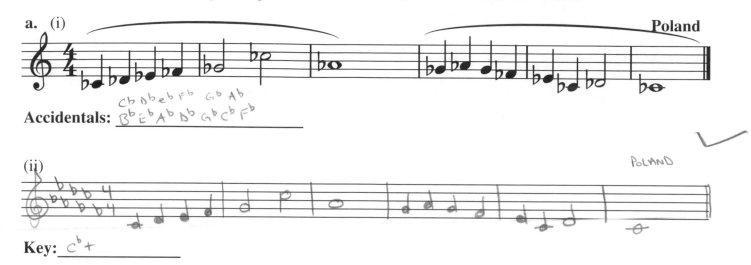

Poland

Accidentals: B♭ E♭ A♭ D♭ G♭ C♭ F♭

(ii)

POLAND

Key: C♭+

b. (i)

France

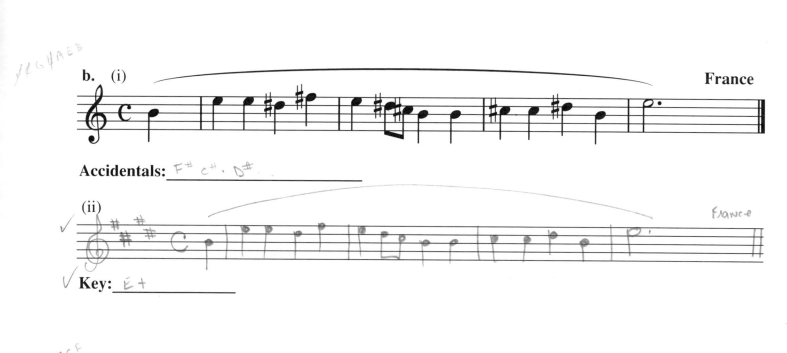

Accidentals: F♯ C♯. D♯

(ii)

France

Key: E+

c. (i) Moderato

Foster

Accidentals: B♭ E♭ A♭ D♭ G♭ ? C ? F

ends on tonic = G♭ :: C♭ also implied

(ii) moderato

Foster

Key: D♭+ ✗ G♭

F# C# G# D# A E B

d. (i)   Germany

Accidentals: ___F# C# G# D#_____ ends on B ∴ A# is implied

(ii)   GERMANY

x✓ Key: ___B+ x✓___

e. (i)   Austria

Accidentals: ___Bb (•)_____

ends on tonic

(ii)   AUSTRIA.

x✓ Key: ___Bb+___

F# C# G# D# A E B

f. (i)   A. Scarlatti

x✓ Accidentals: ___F#1 C# G# A#_____

ends on tonic

(ii)   A. Scarlatti

Key: ___F# +___

Rewriting Minor Key Melodies, using a Key Signature
Melodies based on the minor scale (harmonic form)

UP TO FOUR SHARPS

The melody is based on the minor scale (harmonic form), when the key signature skips **TWO SHARPS.**

Russia

Accidentals: F♯ C♯ . . . A♯

To name the key:

1. Find the **LAST SHARP (A♯),** which is the **LEADING NOTE** (7th note of the scale).
2. Go **UP** a diatonic semitone to the tonic note **B**. Therefore, the melody is in the key of **b minor.**

Russia

Key: b minor

Key: b minor, harmonic form

FIVE OR MORE SHARPS

The melody is also based on the minor scale (harmonic form), when a **DOUBLE SHARP (𝄪)** is used.

England

Accidentals: F𝄪 C♯ G♯ D♯ A♯

To name the key:

1. Find the **DOUBLE SHARP (F𝄪),** which is the **LEADING NOTE.**
2. Go **UP** a diatonic semitone to the tonic note **G♯.** Therefore, the melody is in the key of **g♯ minor.**

England

Key: g♯ minor

Key: g♯ minor, harmonic form

EXERCISES:

3. (i) **PLAY** the following melodies and name the **ACCIDENTALS.**

   (ii) Rewrite each melody, using a **KEY SIGNATURE** and name the **KEY.**

   (iii) Write the corresponding scale, using a **KEY SIGNATURE** and name the **KEY.**

The Jolly Miller

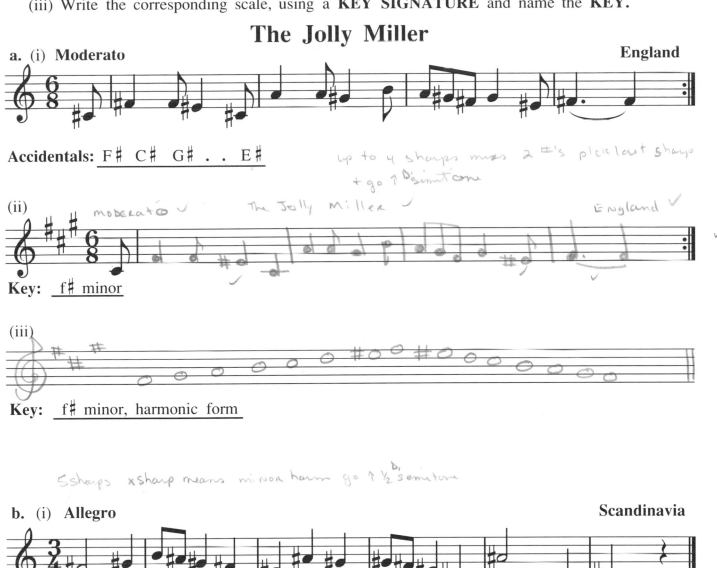

a. (i) **Moderato**   **England**

Accidentals: F♯ C♯ G♯ . . E♯

up to 4 sharps miss 2 ♯'s pick last sharp + go ↑ ¹⁄₂ simitone

(ii)   moderato ✓   The Jolly Miller ✓   England ✓

Key: f♯ minor

(iii)

Key: f♯ minor, harmonic form

5 sharps x sharp means minor harm go ↑ ¹⁄₂ semitone

b. (i) **Allegro**   **Scandinavia**

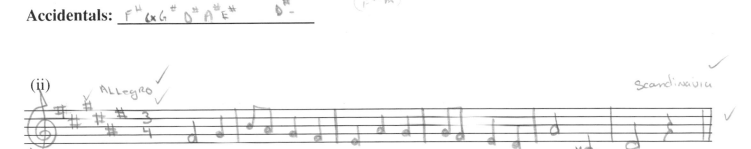

Accidentals: F♯ (xG♯) D♯ A♯ E♯   D♯   (F♯m)

(ii)   allegro ✓   Scandinavia

Key: D♯ minor

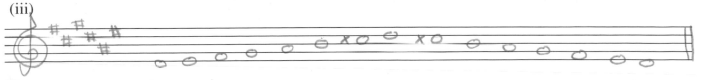

(iii)

Key: D♯ minor Harmonic

UP TO TWO FLATS

The melody is based on the minor scale (harmonic form), when **FLATS** and **SHARPS** are used simultaneously.

Vivace   **France**

Accidentals: B♭   E♭ _____ F♯

To name the key:

1. The key signature is made up of one or two **FLATS.**
2. The **SHARP (F♯)** is the **LEADING NOTE.**
3. Go **UP** a diatonic semitone to the tonic note **G.** Therefore, the melody is in the key of **g minor.**

Vivace   **France**

Key: g minor

Key: g minor, harmonic form

THREE FLATS OR MORE

If a flat is **MISSING** in the order of flats, the melody is also based on the minor scale (harmonic form).

England

Accidentals: B♭ E♭ A♭ . G♭ C♭   *D♭ is missing but in piece D♮*
∴ go up from D♮ a diatonic S.T. to E♭ —

To name the key:

1. The note with the **MISSING FLAT (D)** is the **LEADING NOTE.**   *E♭   G♭ 6♭*
2. Go **UP** a diatonic semitone to the tonic note **E♭.** Therefore, the melody is in the key of **e♭ minor.**

England

Key: e♭ minor

Key: e♭ minor, harmonic form

EXERCISES:

4.　(i) **PLAY** the following melodies and name the **ACCIDENTALS.**
　　(ii) Rewrite each melody, using a **KEY SIGNATURE** and name the **KEY.**
　　(iii) Write the corresponding scale, using a **KEY SIGNATURE** and name the **KEY.**

a. (i)　　　　　　　　　　　　　　　　　　　　　　　　　　　　**England**

Accidentals: ___B♭   ＝♯___

(ii)

Key: ___G minor___

(iii)

Key: ___g minor harmonic___

b. (i)　　　　　　　　　　　　　　　　　　　　　　　　　　　**Schubert**

Accidentals: ___B♭ E♭ A♭ G♭___

Key: ___B♭ minor___

(iii)

Key: ___b♭ minor harm___

Melodies based on the Minor Scale (melodic form)

ALL SHARPS

If the **6th** and **7th NOTES** in a melody are **RAISED**, the corresponding scale is in **minor, MELODIC form.**

Accidentals: F♯   C♯   G♯ . A♯

The **KEY** of a melody based on the minor scale, melodic form, is the **SAME** as the **KEY** of a melody based on the minor scale, harmonic form, with the following **EXCEPTIONS:**

1. Only **ONE ACCIDENTAL** is skipped in the melody, using **SHARPS.**

2. The **LAST SHARP** is the Leading note. Go **UP** a diatonic semitone to find the tonic note **B.**

3. Count **UP** 6 notes from the **TONIC NOTE** (in this instanom anom **B** to **G♯**).

4. If the interval (B to G♯) is a **Major 6th**, the melody is based on the minor scale, melodic form.

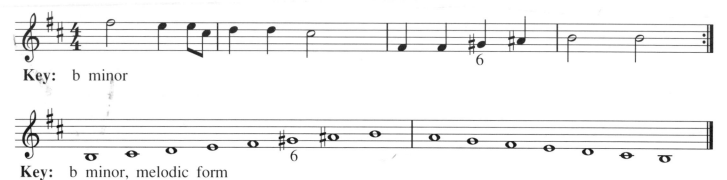

Key: b minor

Key: b minor, melodic form

FLATS

ONE FLAT (d minor)

The melody will have only a **C♯**, which means that **B♭** has been raised (D - B is a Major 6).

TWO FLATS (g minor)

The melody will have a **B♭** and a **F♯**, which means that **E♭** has been raised (G - E is a Major 6).

Accidentals: B♭ _____ F♯   6

Key: g minor   6

Key: g minor, melodic form

THREE FLATS OR MORE

Remember: 1. The skipped flat (D) is the leading note. ②GO ↑ DIATONIC S.T.
2. The interval E♭ to C is a Major 6th.

Scandinavia

Accidentals: B♭ E♭ A♭ (7) G♭ (6)

Scandinavia

Key: e♭ minor

Key: e♭ minor, melodic form

EXERCISES:

5. (i) **PLAY** the following melody and name the **ACCIDENTAL.**
(ii) Rewrite the melody, using a **KEY SIGNATURE** and name the **KEY.**
(iii) Write the corresponding scale, using a **KEY SIGNATURE** and name the **KEY.**

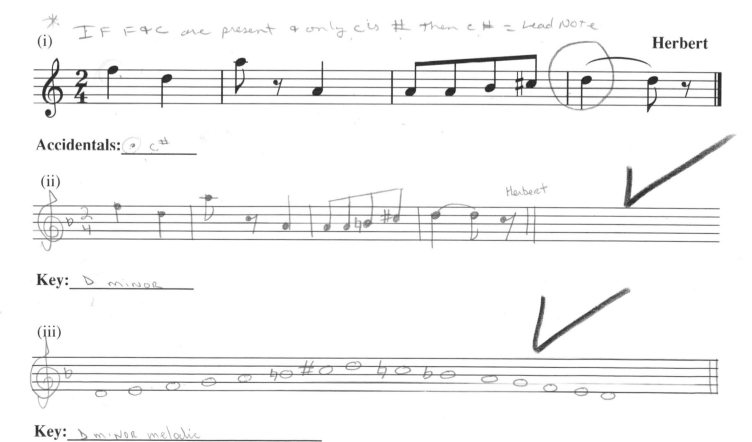

* IF F & C are present & only C is # then C# = Lead NOTE

(i)

Herbert

Accidentals: ⓔ c#

(ii)

Herbert

Key: D minor

(iii)

Key: D minor melodic

Be careful, the following melodies **DO NOT END** on the **TONIC NOTE.**

Invention No. 4

e. (i)

Bach

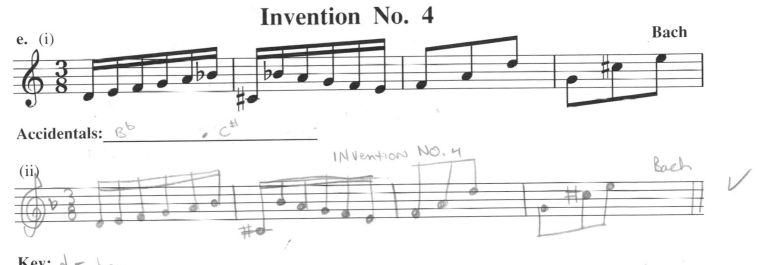

Accidentals: Bb ___ , C# ___

(ii)

INVENTION NO. 4   Bach ✓

Key: d - harm

Waltz from Violin Suite No. 1

f. (i) Scherzando

Ehrhart

Accidentals: F# C# G# b# A# , B#   Go î D.ST. from Last # = C# - Relative = E+ = 4 #'s

(ii) Scherzando   Waltz from Violin Suite No.1   Ehrhart

Key: C# - mel

Là ci darem la mano

g. (i) Andante

Mozart

Accidentals: F# C# G#   A+   F#

(ii) Andante   Là ci darem la mano   Mozart ✓

Key: A+

REVIEW No. 5

100

30

1. (i) Name the **ACCIDENTALS.**

(ii) Rewrite the melody, using a **KEY SIGNATURE** and name the **KEY.**

(iii) Write and name the corresponding scale (Major, minor, harmonic or melodic form), ascending and descending, using a **KEY SIGNATURE** and name the **KEY.**

Hungary

Accidentals: F# C# G# D# A# E#   G C D E = (A♮)

Key: f# — (Rel = A♮)

Key: f# — Melodic.

10

2. Write the following as **HARMONIC INTERVALS** above the given notes.

Major 6th   Major 3rd   Perfect 5th   minor 7th   minor 2nd

10

3. Write the following notes in the treble clef, using **ACCIDENTALS.**

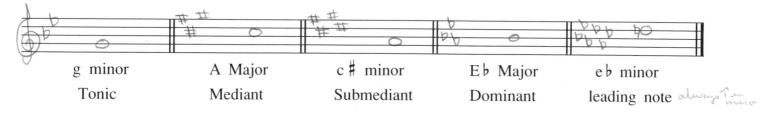

g minor   A Major   c# minor   E♭ Major   e♭ minor
Tonic   Mediant   Submediant   Dominant   leading note

10

4. Add **RESTS** below each bracket to complete the measures.

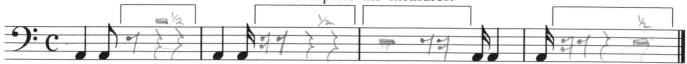

10

5. Add **BAR LINES.**

20   **6.** (i) Name the **ACCIDENTALS.**

(ii) Rewrite the melody, using a **KEY SIGNATURE** and name the **KEY.**

(i)   **Slovakia**

Accidentals: _____ Eb Ab Db Gb .   _____ B is leading Note   C –

(ii)   SLovakia

Key: _C –_____ × (Db)

10   **7.** Add a **TIME SIGNATURE** to the beginning of each melody.

Name the **KEY.**

a.   **J.S. Bach**

Key: _d –_____

b.   **G.F. Handel**

Key: _b –_____

c.   **G.P. Pergolesi**

Key: _C –_____

d.   **G.F. Handel**

Key: _g –_____

e.   **Poldini**

Key: _D+_____

2nds
Harm - Notes touching
- played togeth

2nd's
Mel - Notes do NOT touch
+ ARe played after
each other.

LESSON No. 6
Intervals
The Augmented Interval

The **AUGMENTED SIGN** is written as **"x"** in Canada and as **"A"** or **"Aug."** in the U.S.A.
The **MAJOR SIGN** is written as **"+"** in Canada and as **"M"** or **"Maj."** in the U.S.A.
The **MINOR SIGN** is written as **" - "** in Canada and as **"m"** or **"minor"** in the U.S.A.

To write **AUGMENTED INTERVALS,** follow these three rules:

1. Always identify the Major or Perfect interval first:

Major & Perfect Intervals

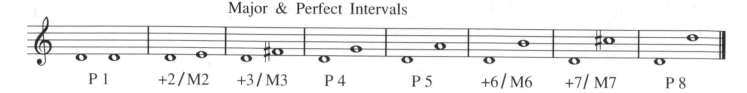

P 1   +2/M2   +3/M3   P 4   P 5   +6/M6   +7/M7   P 8

2. Raise the top note by a **CHROMATIC SEMITONE** (chromatic half step):

Augmented intervals (by raising the top note)

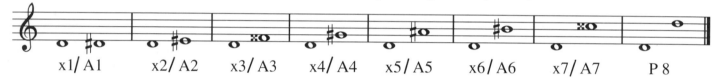

x1/A1   x2/A2   x3/A3   x4/A4   x5/A5   x6/A6   x7/A7   P 8

(If the **P 8** is Augmented, it becomes a compound interval, which will be dealt with in Grade II.)

OR

3. **LOWER** the bottom note by a **CHROMATIC SEMITONE** (chromatic half step):

Augmented intervals (by lowering the bottom note)

x1 / A1   x2/ A2   x3/ A3   x4/ A4   x5 /A5   x6/ A6   x7/A7   P 8

EXERCISES:

Start E Major + go ↑ to Aug.

1. Change each Major or Perfect interval into an **AUGMENTED** interval by raising the top note.
   Name each interval.

a.
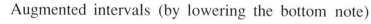

P 4 _____   x4 _____   +3 _____   x3 _____   +6 _____   x 6 _____

b.

+2 _____   x 2 _____   P 5 _____   x 5 _____   P UNISON   X UNISON

2. Write the following **MELODIC** intervals.
   Remember, find the Major or Perfect intervals **FIRST**.

① Count notes ② Bottom is Tonic
eg Db 5bs

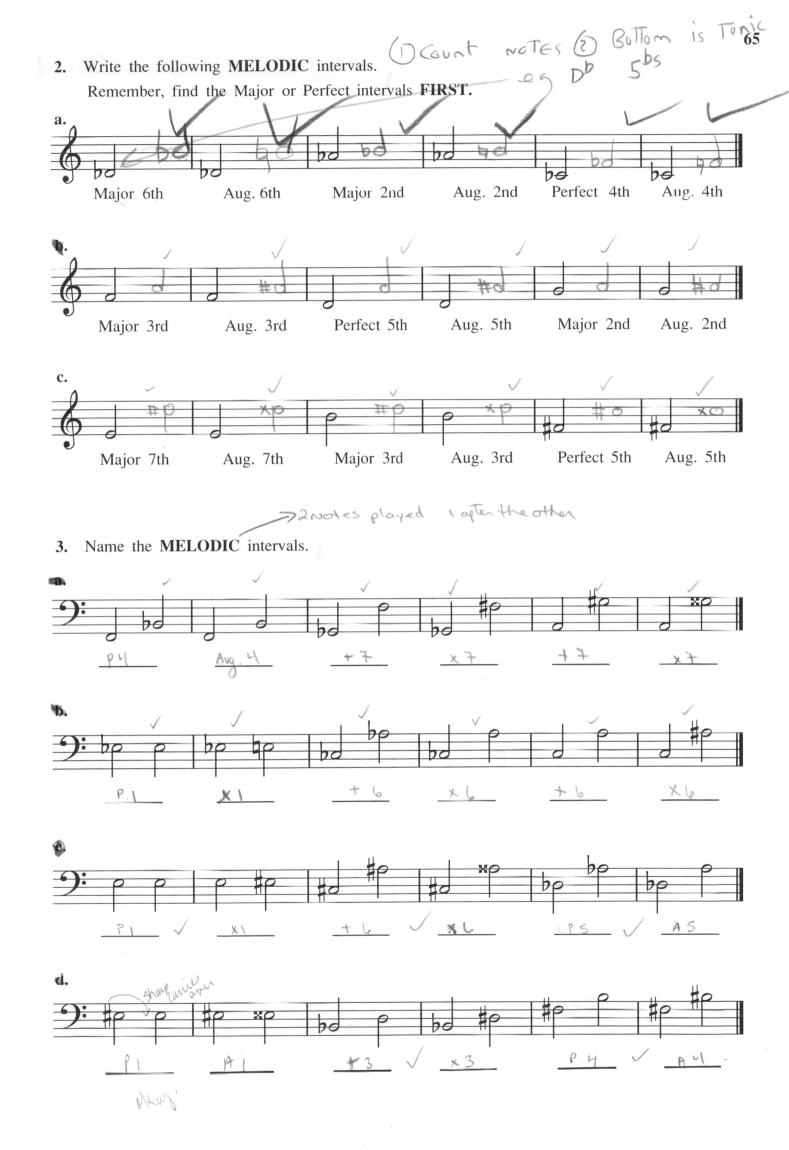

a.

Major 6th   Aug. 6th   Major 2nd   Aug. 2nd   Perfect 4th   Aug. 4th

b.

Major 3rd   Aug. 3rd   Perfect 5th   Aug. 5th   Major 2nd   Aug. 2nd

c.

Major 7th   Aug. 7th   Major 3rd   Aug. 3rd   Perfect 5th   Aug. 5th

→2 notes played 1 after the other

3. Name the **MELODIC** intervals.

a.

P4   Aug. 4   +7   x7   +7   x7

b.

P1   x1   +6   x6   +6   x6

c.

P1   x1   +6   x6   UP5   A5

d.

P1   A1   +3   x3   P4   A4

Okay

66

Change each Major or Perfect interval into an **AUGMENTED** interval by **LOWERING** the bottom note.
Name each interval.

a.

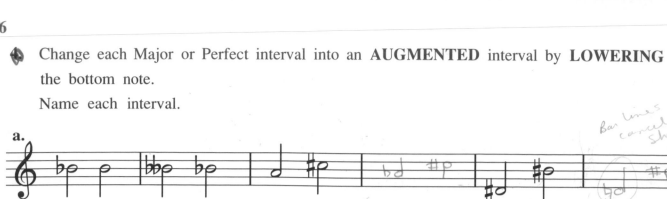

Bar lines cancel sharps

P 1   x1   +3 ✓   x 3   +6   x 6

b.

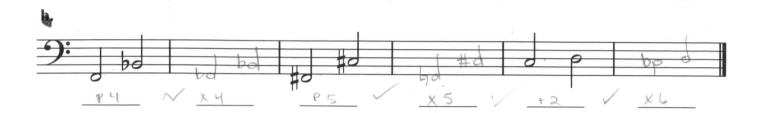

P4   ✓ x 4   P5 ✓   x 5 ✓   +2 ✓   x 6

2 notes played @ same time

5. Name the **HARMONIC** intervals.

a.

+2 ✓   x2   P5 ✓   x5   P4 ✓   x 4

b.

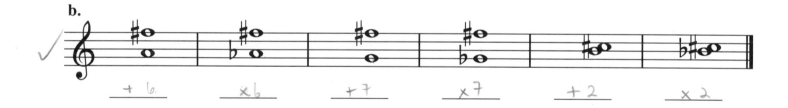

+ 6   x6   +7   x7   +2   x2

c.

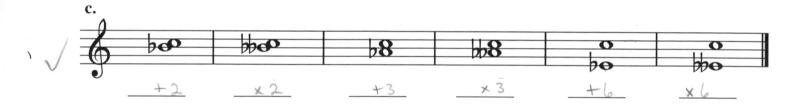

+2   x 2   +3   x 3   +6   x 6

d.

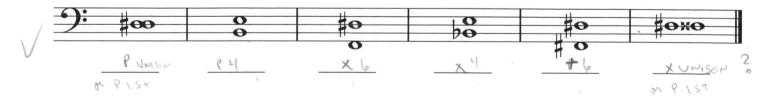

P unison or P 1st   P4   x 6   x 4   +6   x unison or P 1st

e.

x 7   x 5   x 3   P5   +7   +3

The Diminished Interval

> The **DIMINISHED SIGN** is written as "o" in Canada and as "d" or **"dim."** in the U.S.A.

To write **DIMINISHED INTERVALS**, follow these four rules:

1. Always identify the Major or Perfect interval first:

Major & Perfect Intervals

P 1   +2 / M2   +3 / M3   P 4   P 5   +6 / M6   +7 / M7   P 8

2. Change the Major intervals into minor intervals:

Top note lowered a semitone

P 1   -2 / m2   -3 / m3   P 4   P 5   -6 / m6   -7 / m7   P 8

3. **LOWER** the top note of the minor or Perfect interval by a **CHROMATIC SEMITONE:**

Diminished intervals (by lowering the top notes)

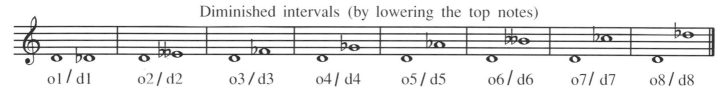

o1 / d1   o2 / d2   o3 / d3   o4 / d4   o5 / d5   o6 / d6   o7 / d7   o8 / d8

4. **RAISE** the bottom note of the minor or Perfect interval by a **CHROMATIC SEMITONE:**

Diminished intervals (by raising the bottom notes)

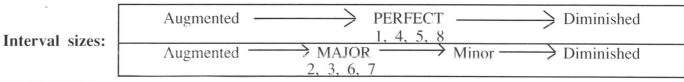

o1 / d1   o2 / d2   o3 / d3   o4 / d4   o5 / d5   o6 / d6   o7 / d7   o8 / d8

Interval sizes:

Augmented ⟶	PERFECT 1, 4, 5, 8	⟶	Diminished
Augmented ⟶	MAJOR 2, 3, 6, 7	⟶ Minor ⟶	Diminished

EXERCISES:

6. Change each interval into a **DIMINISHED** interval by lowering the top note. Name each interval.

a

-6   o6   -7 √ o7   P5 √ o5

b.

-2 √ o2   -3 √ o3   P4 √ o4

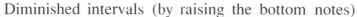
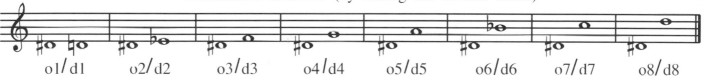
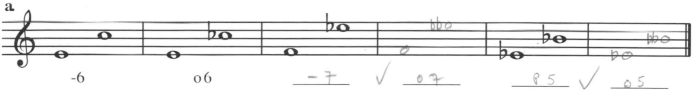

68

7. Write the following **MELODIC** intervals. Remember, find the Major interval first and then the minor interval.

a.

+3 / M3   -3 / m3   o3 / d3   +7 / M7   -7 / m7   o7 / d7

b.

P 5   o5 / d5   P 4   o4 / d4   P 8   o8 / d8

c.

+7 / M7   o3 / d3   +3 / M3   o7 / d7   -3 / m3   -7 / m7

8. Name the **MELODIC** intervals.

a.

+7   -7   o7   +3   -3   o3

b.

P1   o1   P5   o5   P4   o4

c.

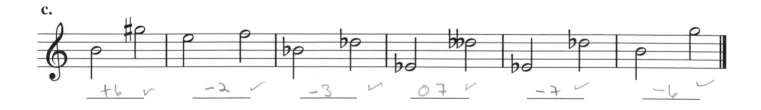

+6   -2   -3   o7   -7   -6

d.

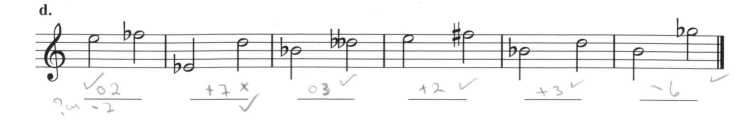

o2   +7   o3   +2   +3   -6

-2

9. Change each minor or Perfect interval into a **DIMINISHED** interval, by **RAISING** the bottom note. Name each **MELODIC** interval.

a.

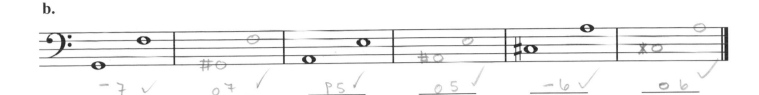

-2   o2   -3 ✓   o3 ✓   P4 ✓   o4 ✓

b.

-7 ✓   o7 ✓   P5 ✓   o5 ✓   -6 ✓   o6 ✓

10. Name the **HARMONIC** intervals.

a.

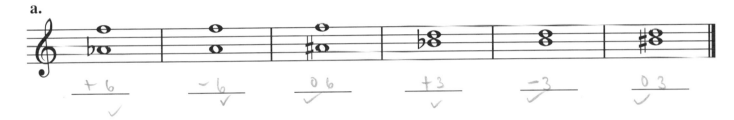

+6 ✓   -6 ✓   o6 ✓   +3 ✓   -3 ✓   o3 ✓

b.

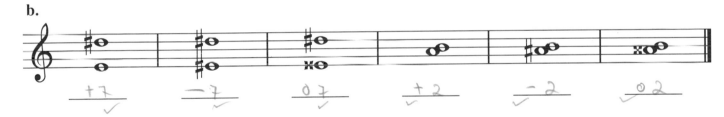

+7 ✓   -7 ✓   o7 ✓   +2 ✓   -2 ✓   o2 ✓

c.

P8 ✓   o8 ✓   P4 ✓   o4 ✓   P5 ✓   o5 ✓

d.

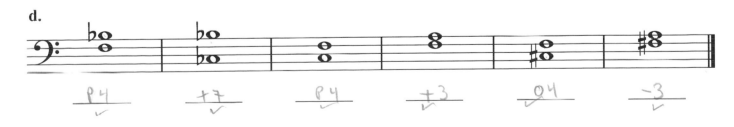

P4 ✓   +7 ✓   P4 ✓   +3 ✓   o4 ✓   -3 ✓

e.

P8 ✓   -7 ✓   o3 ✓   o8 ✓   o7 ✓   o4 ✓

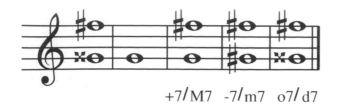

+7/M7 -7/m7 o7/d7

P 5   x5/A5

When solving an interval, where the **LOWER** note has **NO KEY**, change the lower note to a familiar key.

REPLACE the flat or sharp of the lower note and adjust the name of the interval.

+6/M6   +6/M6

When both the top and bottom notes move up a **SEMITONE**, the distance and name of the interval remains the same.

EXERCISES:

11. Change the **LOWER** note to an existing key.
Name the **HARMONIC** intervals.

a.
F F# Fx
A A# A#
-6 +6 +6
+6   -6   o6   A4

b.
P4   o4

c.
+3   -3   o3

d.
P5   o5

e.
+7   -7   o7

f.
-2   o2

g.
F5
A→E=5
AX→EX=5
P5   P5   P5   ? wanting to show a dim 5.

h.
(11)   -3   o3

12. Name the **MELODIC** intervals formed by the bracketed notes.

PLAY each melody.

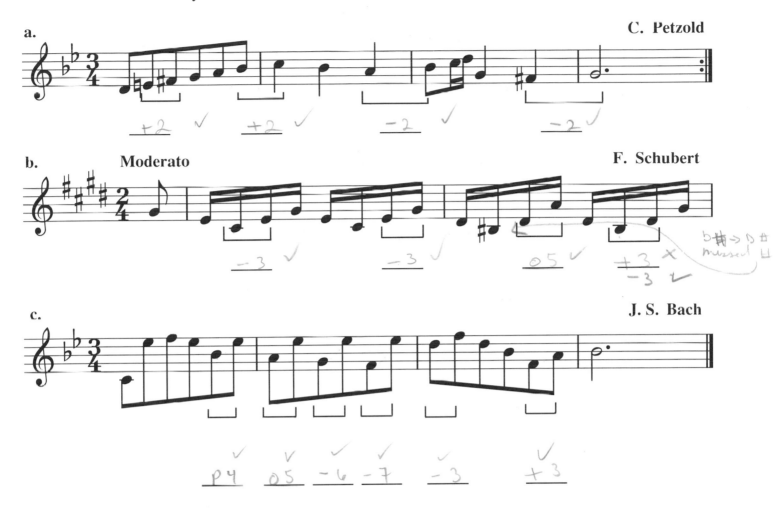

13. Name the **HARMONIC** intervals formed by the bracketed notes.

PLAY each melody.

Inversions of Intervals

1. **INVERSIONS** of **INTERVALS** always add up to **9**.
2. You may move the **LOWER NOTE UP** one octave

   OR

   You may move the **HIGHER NOTE DOWN** one octave

   BUT

   Try to keep the notes on the staff, <u>if possible.</u>
3. The **QUALITY** of the intervals **CHANGE** as follows:
   - (i) **Major** intervals become **minor.**
   - (ii) **minor** intervals become **Major.**
   - (iii) **Perfect** intervals <u>stay</u> **Perfect.**
   - (iv) **Augmented** intervals become **diminished.**
   - (v) **diminished** intervals become **Augmented.**

READ

EXAMPLES:

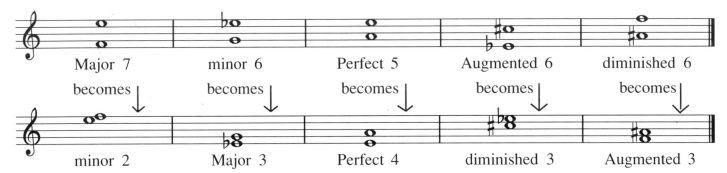

Major 7	minor 6	Perfect 5	Augmented 6	diminished 6
becomes ↓	becomes ↓	becomes ↓	becomes ↓	becomes ↓
minor 2	Major 3	Perfect 4	diminished 3	Augmented 3

EXERCISES: 2nd's would touch.

14. Name the **HARMONIC** intervals. Notice, all intervals are inverted **DOWN.**

a.

Aug 5   Dim 4   +3   -6   -7   +2

b.

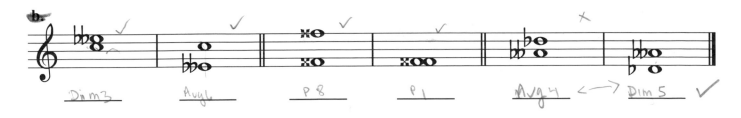

Dim 3   Aug 6   P 8   P 1   Aug 4 → Dim 5

c.

Dim 5   Aug 4   +2   x7   x1   D8

Another **METHOD** of **IDENTIFYING** intervals is to count the **SEMITONES** (half steps).

EXAMPLE:

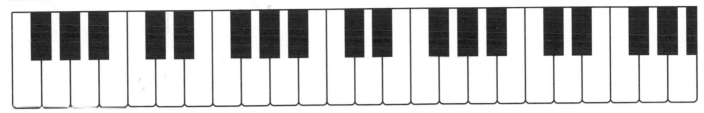

Intervals:	P 1	-2/m2	+2/M2	-3/m3	+3/M3	P 4	P 5	-6/m6	+6/M6	-7/m7	+7/M7	P 8
Semitones: (half steps)	0	1	2	3	4	5	7	8	9	10	11	12

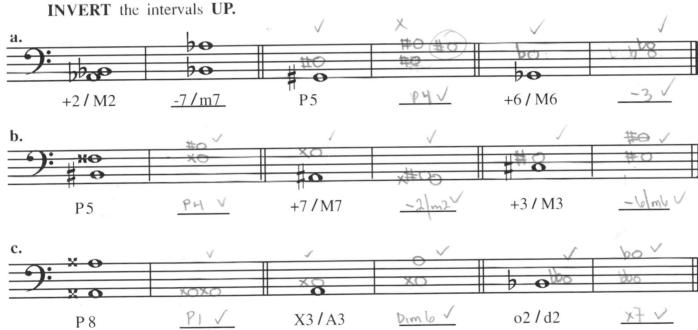

When a **SEMITONE** is **ADDED** to a Major or Perfect interval, it becomes **AUGMENTED**.
When a **SEMITONE** is **TAKEN AWAY** from a minor or Perfect interval, it becomes **DIMINISHED**.

EXERCISES:

15. Write the following as **HARMONIC** intervals, by **COUNTING** the **SEMITONES**.
    INVERT the intervals **UP**.

a.

+2 / M2   -7 / m7   P 5   P4 ✓   +6 / M6   -3 ✓

b.

P 5   P4 ✓   +7 / M7   -2/m2 ✓   +3 / M3   -6/m6 ✓

c.

P 8   P1 ✓   X3 / A3   Dim 6 ✓   o2 / d2   x7 ✓

16. Name the **INTERVALS** formed by the bracketed notes. Count by semitones.

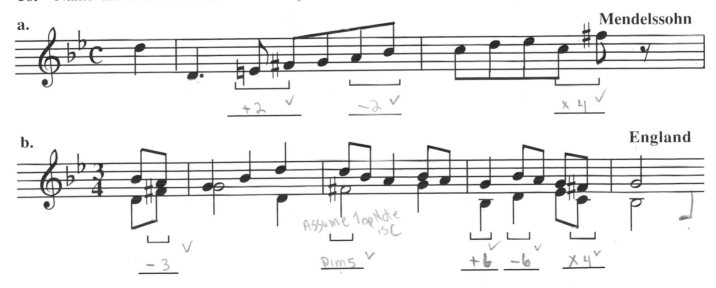

a.   **Mendelssohn**

+2 ✓   -2 ✓   X 4 ✓

b.   **England**

Assume Top Note is C

-3 ✓   Dim5 ✓   +6 ✓ -6 ✓ X 4 ✓

17. Write the following as **MELODIC** intervals.
INVERT each interval and name each inversion.

a.

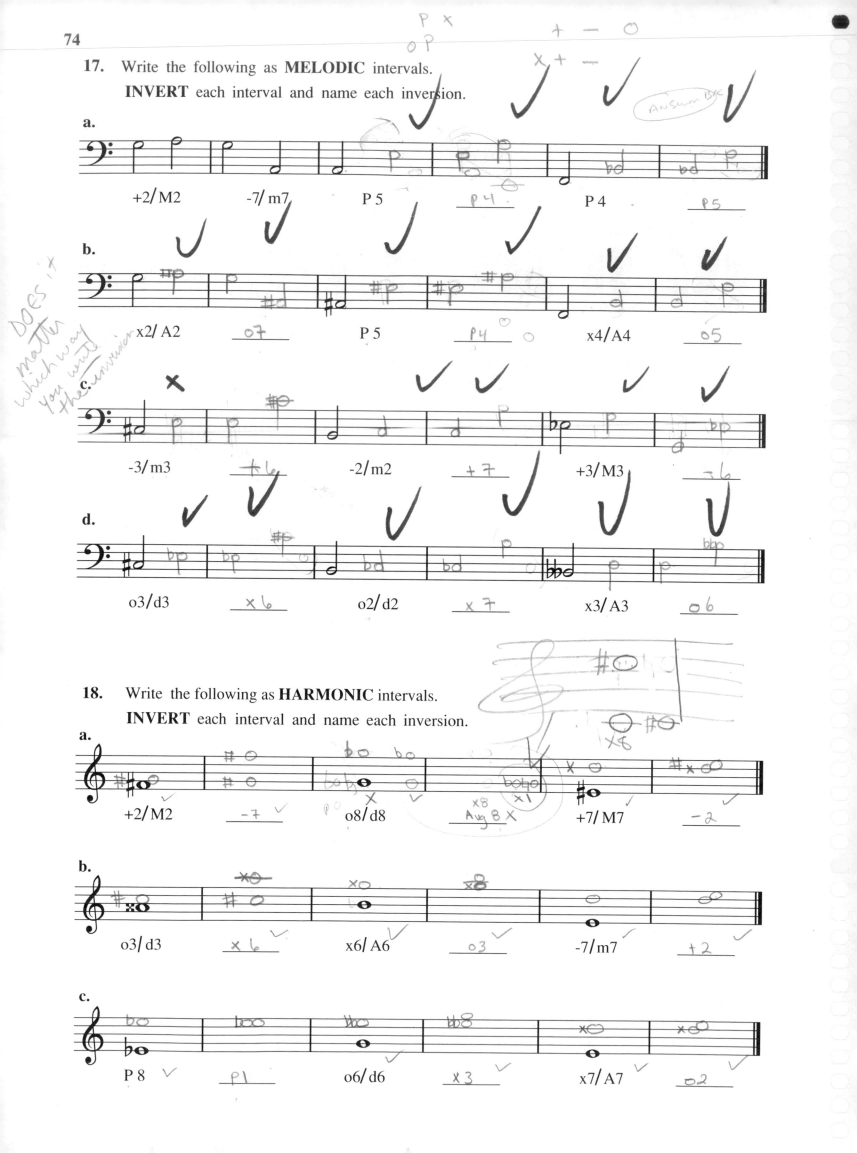

+2/ M2   -7/ m7   P 5   P 4   P 4   P 5

b.

x2/ A2   o7   P 5   P 4   x4/ A4   o5

c.

-3/ m3   +6   -2/ m2   +7   +3/ M3   -6

d.

o3/ d3   x6   o2/ d2   x7   x3/ A3   o6

18. Write the following as **HARMONIC** intervals.
INVERT each interval and name each inversion.

a.

+2/ M2   -7   o8/ d8   Aug 8   +7/ M7   -2

b.

o3/ d3   x6   x6/ A6   o3   -7/ m7   +2

c.

P 8   P1   o6/ d6   x3   x7/ A7   o2

19. Name the **HARMONIC** intervals formed by the bracketed notes.

 PLAY each melody.

a. Finland

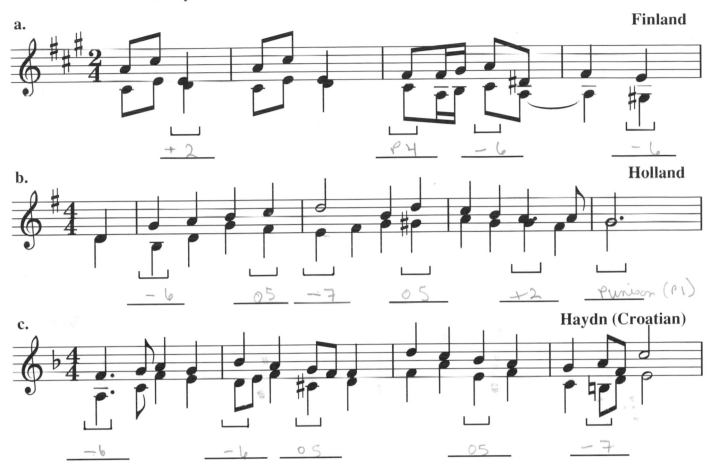

b. Holland

c. Haydn (Croatian)

20. Name the **MELODIC** intervals formed by the bracketed notes.

 PLAY each melody.

a. Czerny

b. Scandinavia

c. C. Debussy

REVIEW No. 6

$\overline{100}$

15

1. Name the **HARMONIC** intervals.

a.

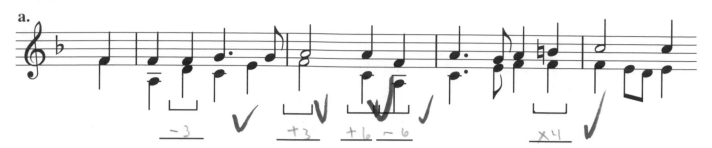

-3 ✓   +3 +6 -6 x4 ✓

b. INVERT the above bracketed intervals and **RENAME** them. Use **WHOLE NOTES.**

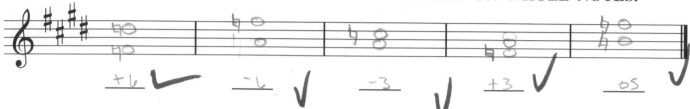

+6 ✓   -6 ✓   -3 ✓   +3 ✓   o5 ✓

10

2. Add **BAR LINES.** Be careful!

a.

b.

10

3. Add **RESTS** below the brackets to complete the measures.

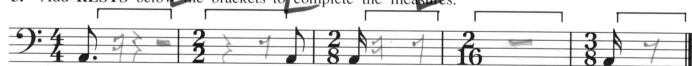

20

4. (i) Name the **ACCIDENTALS.**

(ii) Rewrite the melody, using a **KEY SIGNATURE** and name the **KEY.**

(i)

P.I. Tchaikovsky

Accidentals: ___Ab Eb Db Gb Bb___

(ii)

P.I. Tchaikovsky

Key: ___Db +___

15 **5.** Write the following scales in the bass clef, ascending and descending, using **ACCIDENTALS.**
Mark the **SEMITONES** with a slur.

a. C♭ Major in **4/4** TIME, using quarter notes.

b. d♯ minor, harmonic form, in **2/2** TIME, using half notes.

c. a♭ minor, melodic form, in **2/4** TIME, using eighth notes.

10 **6.** Write **SUBMEDIANT** notes for each of the following minor keys (melodic form).
Use **KEY SIGNATURES.**

      f♯ minor   e♭ minor   e minor   c minor   a♯ minor

10 **7.** Rewrite the notes, **GROUPING** them according to the **TIME SIGNATURES.**

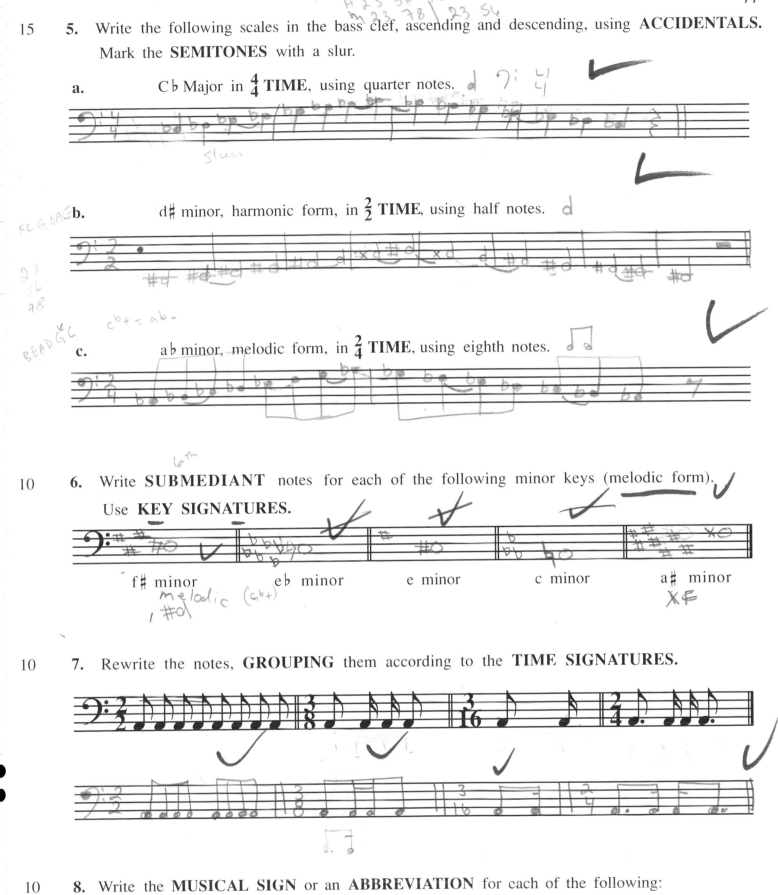

10 **8.** Write the **MUSICAL SIGN** or an **ABBREVIATION** for each of the following:

crescendo			*piano*		*p*
decrescendo			*pianissimo*		*pp*
forte		*f*	*rallentando*		
mezzo forte		*mf*	*ritardando*		*Ritard.*
mezzo piano		*mp*	*Da Capo*		

LESSON No. 7

RHYTHM

Compound Duple Time

6/16

This time signature groups **2 BEATS** to a measure.

The top number shows the **6 PULSES** to a measure, which are grouped in threes: ♪. (3) + ♪. (3) = 6.

The bottom number shows that the sixteenth note (♪) or sixteenth rest (₹) receive one pulse.

6/8

This time signature groups **2 BEATS** to a measure.

The top number shows the **6 PULSES** to a measure, which are grouped in threes: ♩. (3) + ♩. (3) = 6.

The bottom number shows that the eighth note (♪) or eighth rest (₹) receive one pulse.

6/4

This time signature groups **2 BEATS** to a measure.

The top number shows the **6 PULSES** to a measure, which are grouped in threes: ♩. (3) + ♩. (3) = 6.

The bottom number shows that the quarter note (♩) or quarter rest (𝄽) receive one pulse.

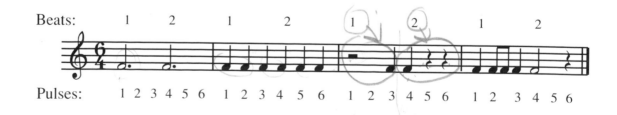

When writing rests, always combine a **STRONG** and a **WEAK** pulse or a **MEDIUM** and a **WEAK** pulse into **ONE REST.**

NEVER combine two weak pulses into **ONE REST.**

EXERCISES:

1. Mark the **ACCENTS** and write the **PULSES** below each rhythm.

In **COMPOUND DUPLE TIME** the beats are usually divided in a **STRONG** and a **WEAK** beat:

When writing rests in **COMPOUND DUPLE TIME,** always combine the first three pulses or the last three pulses into **ONE REST.**

EXERCISES:

3. Mark the **ACCENTS** and write the **BEATS** below each rhythm.

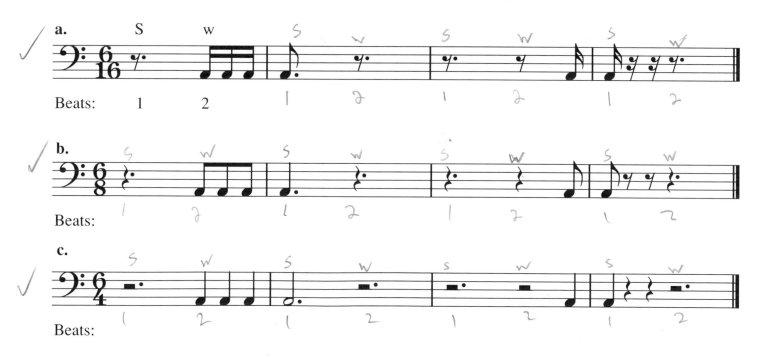

4. Add **ONE REST** below each bracket to complete the measures.

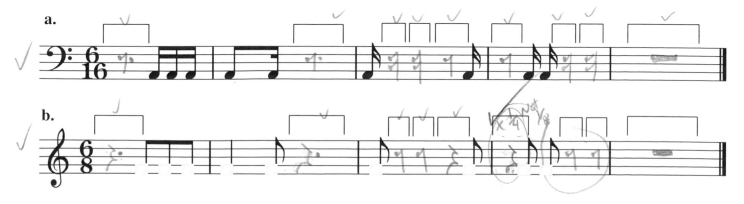

5. Add a **TIME SIGNATURE** to the beginning of each staff.

6. Add **BAR LINES.**

Compound Triple Time

$\frac{9}{16}$

This time signature groups **3 BEATS** to a measure.

The top number shows **9 PULSES** to a measure, which are grouped in threes: ♪.(3) + ♪.(3) + ♪.(3) = 9.

The bottom number shows that the sixteenth note (♪) or sixteenth rest (¼) receives one pulse.

Notice the last measure. This is how 3 beats (9 pulses) of sound are written for $\frac{9}{16}$.

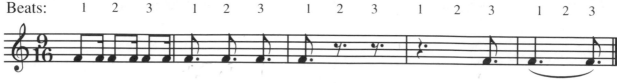

$\frac{9}{8}$

This time signature groups **3 BEATS** to a measure.

The top number shows **9 PULSES** to a measure, which are grouped in threes: ♩.(3) + ♩.(3) + ♩.(3) = 9.

The bottom number shows that the eighth note (♪) or eighth rest (⅞) receives one pulse.

Notice the last measure. This is how 3 beats (9 pulses) of sound are written for $\frac{9}{8}$.

$\frac{9}{4}$

This time signature groups **3 BEATS** to a measure.

The top number shows **9 PULSES** to a measure, which are grouped in threes: ♩.(3) + ♩.(3) + ♩.(3) = 9.

The bottom number shows that the quarter note (♩) or quarter rest (𝄽) receives one pulse.

Notice the last measure. This is how 3 beats (9 pulses) of sound are written for $\frac{9}{4}$.

EXERCISES:

7. Add **BAR LINES.**

8. Add **ONE REST** below each bracket to complete the measures.

In Compound Triple Time the **BEATS** are usually divided in **STRONG, WEAK, WEAK.**

Accents:

 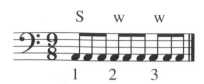 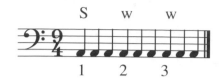

Beats: 1 2 3   1 2 3   1 2 3

When writing rests, always combine the **STRONG** and the **WEAK** beats into **ONE REST.**

NEVER combine two weak beats into one rest. (Remember the rules for pulses and rests on p.79.)

Accents: S w w   S w w   S w w   S w w   S w w   S w w

  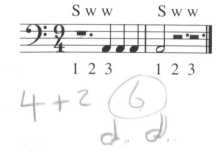

Beats: 1 2 3   1 2 3   1 2 3   1 2 3   1 2 3   1 2 3

4 + 2 ⑥
♩. ♩.

EXERCISES:

9. Mark the **ACCENTS** and write the **BEATS** below each rhythm.

a.

Beats: 1   2   3

b.

Beats:

c.

Beats:

10. Write **ONE REST** below each bracket to complete the measures.

a.

b.

wrong dot placement · above 3rd line

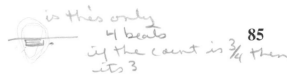
is this only
4 beats
if the count is 3/4 then
its 3

c.

d.

e.

11. Add a **TIME SIGNATURE** to the beginning of each staff.

a.

b.

c.
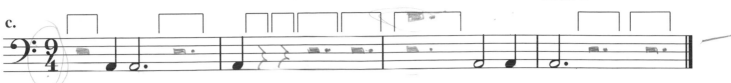

d.

e.

Compound Quadruple Time

12/16

GROUP
4 ♪'s

This time signature groups **4 BEATS** to a measure.

The top number shows **12 PULSES** to a measure, which are grouped in threes: ♪.(3) + ♪.(3) + ♪.(3) + ♪.(3) = 12.

The bottom number shows that the sixteenth note (♪) or sixteenth rest (𝄽) receives **ONE PULSE.**

A dotted half note (♩.) expresses 4 beats (♪.), 12 pulses (♪).

Beats: 1   2   3   4   1   2   3   4   1   2   3   4

Pulses: 1 2 3 4 5 6 7 8 9 10 11 12   1 2 3 4 5 6 7 8 9 10 11 12   1 2 3 4 5 6 7 8 9 10 11 12

12/8

4 ♩.'s

This time signature groups **4 BEATS** to a measure.

The top number shows **12 PULSES** to a measure, which are grouped in threes: ♩.(3) + ♩.(3) + ♩.(3) + ♩.(3) = 12.

The bottom number shows that the eighth note (♪) or eighth rest (𝄾) receives **ONE PULSE.**

A dotted whole note (𝅝.) expresses 4 beats (♩.), 12 pulses (♪).

Beats: 1   2   3   4   1   2   3   4   1   2   3   4

Pulses: 1 2 3 4 5 6 7 8 9 10 11 12   1 2 3 4 5 6 7 8 9 10 11 12   1 2 3 4 5 6 7 8 9 10 11 12

12/4

4 ♩.'s

This time signature groups **4 BEATS** to a measure.

The top number shows **12 PULSES** to a measure, which are grouped in threes: ♩.(3) + ♩.(3) + ♩.(3) + ♩.(3) = 12.

The bottom number shows that the quarter note (♩) or quarter rest (𝄽) receives **ONE PULSE.**

A dotted breve note (𝅜.) expresses 4 beats (♩.), 12 pulses (♩).

Beats: 1   2   3   4   1   2   3   4   1   2   3   4

Pulses: 1 2 3 4 5 6 7 8 9 10 11 12   1 2 3 4 5 6 7 8 9 10 11 12   1 2 3 4 5 6 7 8 9 10 11 12

EXERCISES:

12. Add a **TIME SIGNATURE** to the beginning of each staff.

a.

b.

c.

d.

13. Add **BAR LINES.**

a.

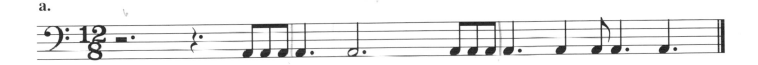

b.

c.

d.

In Compound Quadruple Time the **BEATS** are usually divided in **STRONG, WEAK MEDIUM, WEAK.**

When writing rests, always combine the **STRONG** and **WEAK**, or the **MEDIUM** and **WEAK** beats into **ONE REST.**

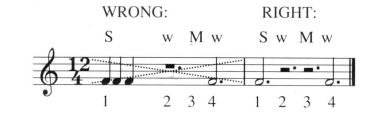

NEVER combine a **WEAK** and a **MEDIUM** beat into **ONE REST.** (Remember the rules for pulses and rests on page 79.)

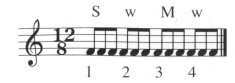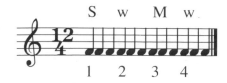

EXERCISES:

14. Mark the **ACCENTS** and write the **BEATS** below each rhythm.

a.

Beats: 1 2 3 4

b.

Beats:

c.

Beats:

15. Add **ONE REST** below each bracket to complete the measures.

Thirty - Second Notes

The various beats of the **THIRTY - SECOND** note are:

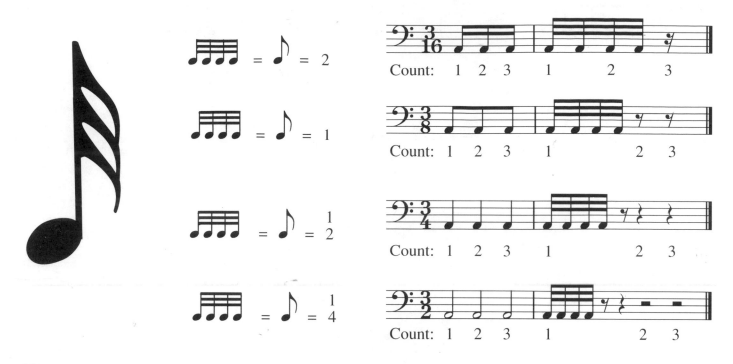

THIRTY - SECOND notes are available in both **SIMPLE** and **COMPOUND TIME.**

EXERCISES:

16. Add a **TIME SIGNATURE** to the beginning of each staff.

17. Add **BAR LINES.**

a.

b.

c.

d.

18. Rewrite the notes, **GROUPING** them according to the time signature.

a.

b.

Thirty - Second Rests

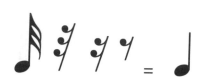

When adding more than one rest to complete a beat or measure, always build **OUTWARD** from the given **NOTE VALUE,** building to the eighth note (♪), then the quarter note (♩), then the half note (𝅗𝅥), then the dotted half note (𝅗𝅥.), and then the whole note (𝅝).

if given: if given:

build forward   build backward

EXAMPLES:

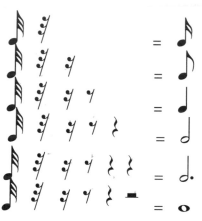

EXERCISES:

19. Fill in the missing **RESTS.**

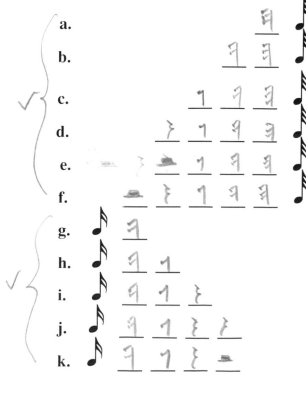

a.		= ♪
b.		= ♪
c.		= ♩
d.		= 𝅗𝅥
e.		= 𝅗𝅥.
f.		= 𝅝
g.		= ♪
h.		= ♩
i.		= 𝅗𝅥
j.		= 𝅗𝅥.
k.		= 𝅝
l.		= ♪
m.		= ♪
n.		= ♩
o.		= 𝅗𝅥
p.		= 𝅗𝅥.
q.		= 𝅝
r.		= ♪
s.		= ♩
t.		= 𝅗𝅥
u.		= 𝅗𝅥.
v.		= 𝅝

EXAMPLE:

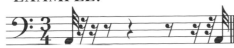

Notice how we build up to **ONE BEAT** each from two directions at the same time.

EXERCISES:

20. Add **ONE REST** below each bracket to complete the measures.

More on the Triplet in Simple Time

TRIPLET quarter notes (♩), eighth notes (♪), sixteenth notes (♬) and thirty-second notes (♬) are possible in **ANY SIMPLE TIME SIGNATURE:**

A **TRIPLET** is **NOT** always equal to one beat. It is possible that three notes can be performed in the time of **HALF** a beat:

EXERCISES:

21. Add **ONE TRIPLET** below each bracket to complete the measures.

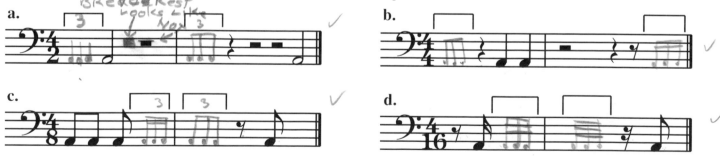

22. Add **ONE REST** below each bracket to complete the measures.

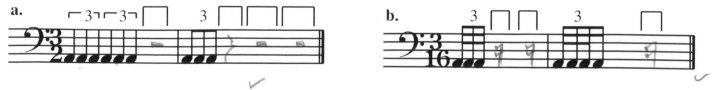

Some **VARIATIONS** on the most commonly used **TRIPLETS** are:

When a **BEAM** is added, it **HALVES** the value of the notes in **ANY** time signature and in **ANY** grouping of notes.

EXAMPLES: $\frac{2}{2}$ = 1 ;   = $\frac{1}{2}$;   = $\frac{1}{4}$;   = $\frac{1}{8}$

Or, when a **BEAM** is taken away, it **DOUBLES** the value of the notes in **ANY** time signature and in **ANY** grouping of notes.

EXAMPLES: $\frac{4}{4}$ = $\frac{1}{2}$;   = 1 ;   = 2 ;   = 4.

EXERCISES:

23. Add **BAR LINES.**

More Irregular Note Groupings
The Duplet and the Quadruplet

Generally, the and the

are available

ONLY

in **COMPOUND TIME**

A **DUPLET** is where 2 notes are played in the time of 3 notes:

A **QUADRUPLET** is where 4 notes are played in the time of 3 notes:

*(1)   *(2)

* These concepts will change at a future date to: (1)   (2)

EXERCISES:

24. Add a **TIME SIGNATURE** to the beginning of each staff.

a.

b.

c.

97

25. Add **BAR LINES.**

a.

26. Add **ONE REST** below each bracket to complete the measures.

a.

Irregular Groupings of FIVE, SIX and SEVEN

SIMPLE TIME

The normal breakdown of the beat in **SIMPLE TIME** is in **2's** and **4's:**

Quintuplet

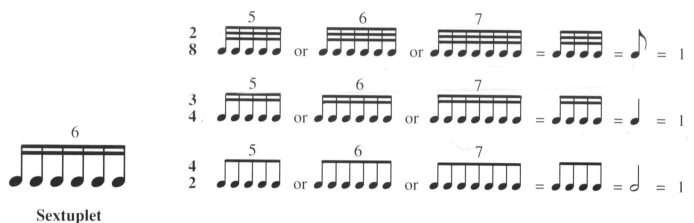

Any other grouping is considered to be **IRREGULAR:**

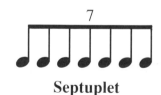

Sextuplet

COMPOUND TIME

The normal breakdown of the beat in **COMPOUND TIME** is in **3's** and **6's:**

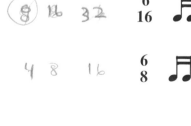

Septuplet

Any other grouping is considered to be **IRREGULAR:**

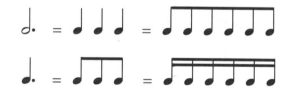

Groupings of **9, 10, 11** and **12** are also possible in **SIMPLE** and **COMPOUND TIME.**
Remember, when solving **TIME SIGNATURES:**

1. The **NUMBER** indicated, is the number of notes in that group.

2. Always consider the beats in **OTHER MEASURES**, which may not contain an irregular grouping.

EXERCISES:

27. Add a **TIME SIGNATURE** to the beginning of each staff.

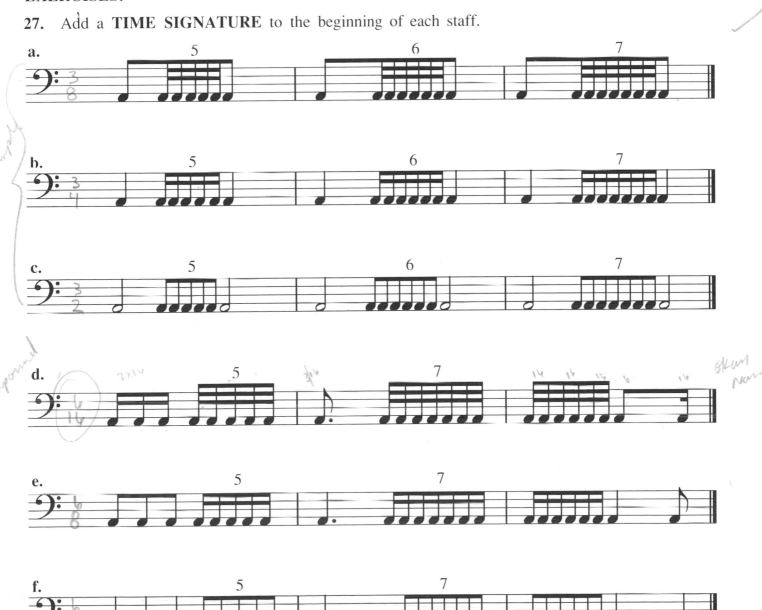

28. Add **BAR LINES.**

a.

b.

c.

d.

29. Add **ONE REST** below each bracket to complete the measures.

a.

b.

c.
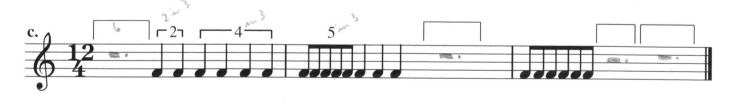

d.

30. Add a **TIME SIGNATURE** to the beginning of each staff.

a.

b.

c.

d.

e.

f.

g.

h.

31. Add **RESTS** below each bracket to complete the measures.

32. Add **STEMS** to the note heads to complete each measure. Do **NOT** use dots or rests. Use **DUPLETS**, **TRIPLETS** and other **NOTE GROUPINGS** where possible.

Rhythmic excerpts from composed music

33. Add a **TIME SIGNATURE** to the beginning of each staff.

REVIEW No. 7

100

20 **1.** Write the following scales ascending and descending in whole notes, using a **KEY SIGNATURE.** Begin each scale on the **TONIC** note.

   a.   the Major scale, with **A♭** as its subdominant

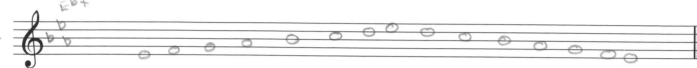

   b.   the minor scale, harmonic form, with **E♭** as its mediant

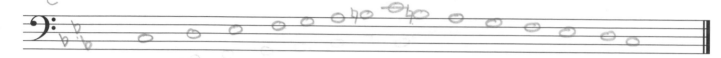

   c.   the minor scale, melodic form, with **F** as its submediant

20 **2.** (i) Name the **ACCIDENTALS** of the following melody.

    (ii) Rewrite the melody, using a **KEY SIGNATURE** and name the **KEY.**

   (iii) Write and name the corresponding scale (Major, minor - harmonic or melodic form), ascending and descending, using a **KEY SIGNATURE** and name the **KEY.**

Allegrissimo
                                                        D. Scarlatti

Accidentals: _____

Key: _____

Key: _____

20

3. Add **RESTS** below each bracket to complete the measures.

20

4. Add a **TIME SIGNATURE** to the beginning of each measure.

20

5.

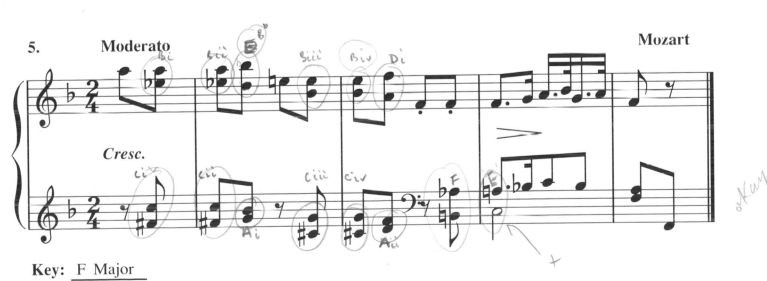

Key: F Major

LABEL and **CIRCLE** each of the following:

A. Two minor 3rd's; B. Four Augmented 4th's; C. Four diminished 5th's;

D. Two minor 6th's; E. One Major 6th; F. One diminished 7th.

LESSON No. 8

Inversions of Triads
Triads in SOLID FORM

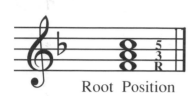

Root Position

The **TRIAD** can be built on any degree of a Major or minor scale. The lowest note is known as the **ROOT.** The middle note is known as the **THIRD.** The highest note is known as the **FIFTH.**

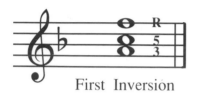

First Inversion

In the **1st INVERSION** the **ROOT** (lowest note) moves **UP** one octave.

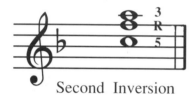

Second Inversion

In the **2nd INVERSION,** the **ROOT** and the **3rd NOTE** move **UP** one octave.

Triads in BROKEN FORM

F Major Triad

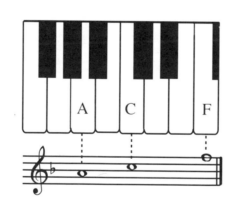

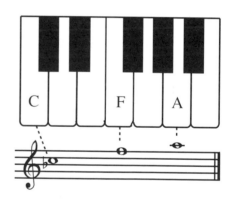

EXERCISES:

if 1st is 2 lines + 1 space
2 " 2 space + 1 line

① **INVERT** the following **TRIADS** and state the **POSITION.**

Root   1st Inv.   2nd Inv.   Root   1st   2nd   Root   1st   2nd

b.

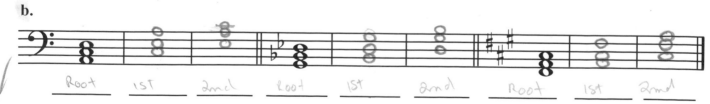

Root   1st   2nd   Root   1st   2nd   Root   1st   2nd

2. Write the following triads in **ROOT POSITION** and name the **ROOT** and **KEY.**

a.

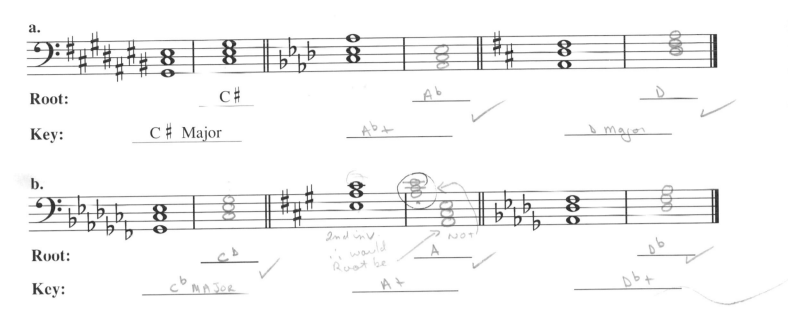

Root: C#   Ab   D

Key: C# Major   Ab+   D major

b.

Root: Cb   A   Db

Key: Cb MAJOR   A+   Db+

2nd inv. would Root be   Not

3. Write the following triads in **ROOT POSITION** and name the **ROOT.** Write the **KEY SIGNATURE** for the given keys.

a.

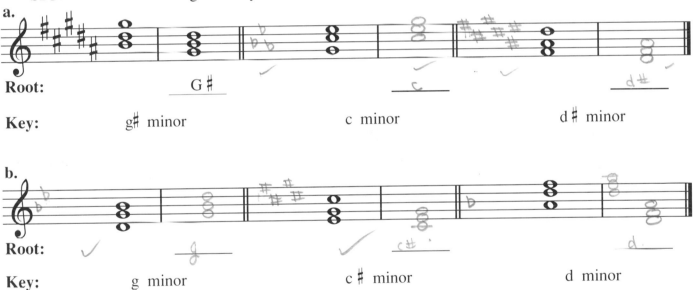

Root: G#   c   d#

Key: g# minor   c minor   d# minor

b.

Root: g   c#   d

Key: g minor   c# minor   d minor

4. Write the following triads in the **BASS CLEF,** using a **KEY SIGNATURE.**

a.

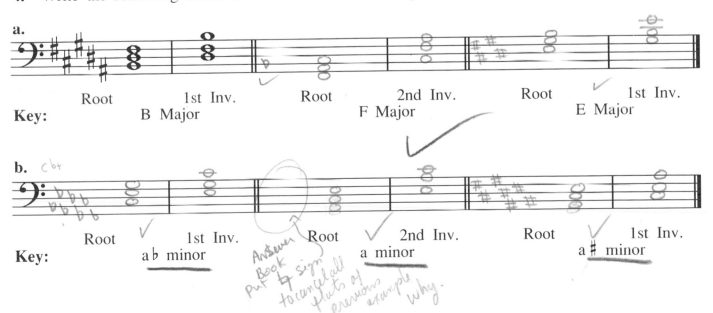

Root   1st Inv.   Root   2nd Inv.   Root   1st Inv.

Key: B Major   F Major   E Major

b. Cb+

Root   1st Inv.   Root   2nd Inv.   Root   1st Inv.

Key: ab minor   a minor   a# minor

Answer Book Put # sign to cancel all flats of previous example why.

108

5. Write the following **TRIADS** in the treble clef, using a **KEY SIGNATURE.**

C Major	Cb Major	C# Major	Ab Major	f minor
Root	1st Inv.	2nd Inv.	1st Inv.	2nd Inv.

6. Name the **KEY SIGNATURE** found in each key. *NAME #'s or b's found in each key*

Add **ACCIDENTALS** where necessary to complete the triads.

(Note: When three accidentals in a triad interfere, the highest accidental is written closest to the note. The lowest accidental is written next farthest from the note. The middle accidental is written the farthest away from the note.)

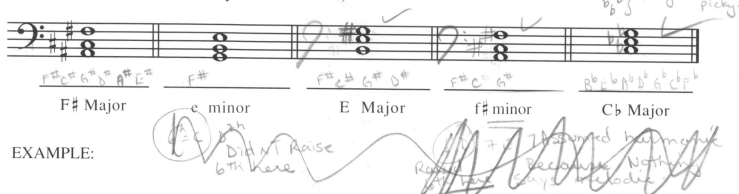

F# Major	e minor	E Major	f# minor	Cb Major

EXAMPLE:

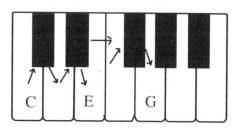

In Major triads, from the **ROOT** to the **3rd note** is always a **MAJOR 3RD** or equal to **4 SEMITONES (C - E).**

From the **3RD NOTE** to the **5TH NOTE** is always a **minor 3rd**, or equal to **3 SEMITONES (E - G).**

From the **ROOT** to the **5TH NOTE** is always a **Perfect 5th**, or equal to **7 SEMITONES (C - G).**

EXERCISES:

7. Write the following Major triads in **ROOT** position, counting semitones. Add **ACCIDENTALS.**

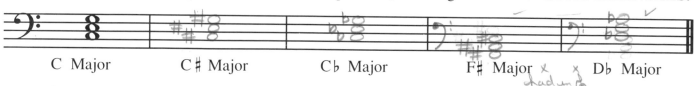

C Major	C# Major	Cb Major	F# Major	Db Major

8. Write the following Major triads by counting the semitones. Add **ACCIDENTALS.**

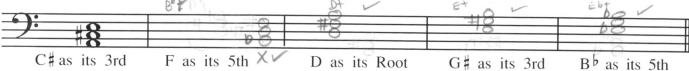

C# as its 3rd	F as its 5th	D as its Root	G# as its 3rd	Bb as its 5th

9. Add **ACCIDENTALS** to form Major triads.

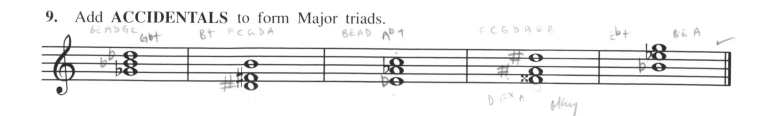

EXAMPLE:

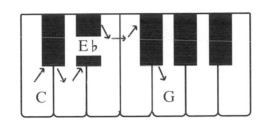

In minor triads, from the **ROOT** to the **3RD NOTE** is always a **minor 3rd**, or equal to **3 SEMITONES (C - E♭)**. From the **3RD** to the **5TH NOTE** is always a **Major 3RD**, or equal to **4 SEMITONES (E♭ - G)**. From the **ROOT** to the **5TH NOTE** is always a **Perfect 5th**, or equal to **7 SEMITONES (C - G)**.

EXERCISES:

10. Write the following minor triads in **ROOT** position, by counting **SEMITONES.**

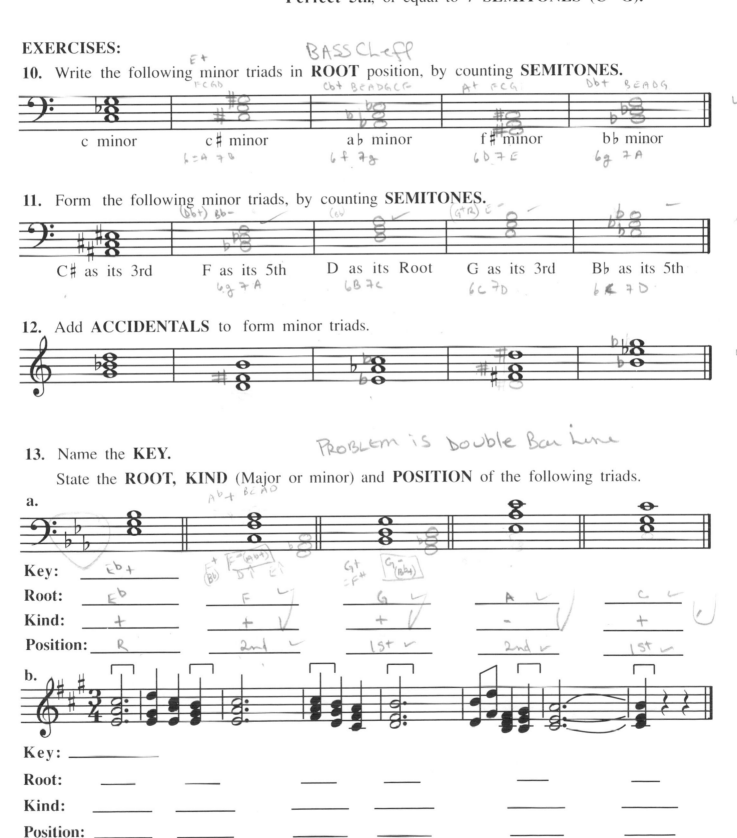

c minor   c♯ minor   a♭ minor   f♯ minor   b♭ minor

11. Form the following minor triads, by counting **SEMITONES.**

C♯ as its 3rd   F as its 5th   D as its Root   G as its 3rd   B♭ as its 5th

12. Add **ACCIDENTALS** to form minor triads.

13. Name the **KEY.**

State the **ROOT, KIND** (Major or minor) and **POSITION** of the following triads.

a.

Key: _____
Root: _____
Kind: _____
Position: _____

b.

Key: _____
Root: _____ _____ _____ _____ _____
Kind: _____ _____ _____ _____ _____
Position: _____ _____ _____ _____ _____

100

REVIEW No. 8

15   **1.** Name the **KEY** of the following key signatures. Name the **TECHNICAL DEGREE** of each note.

Key: C# +   B♭ +   D# −   B♭ −   G +

Degree: TONIC   Leading Note   Leading Note   submediant   Submediant

10   **2.** Write the following scales in eighth notes, **ASCENDING** only.

USING ACCIDENTALS: **USING A KEY SIGNATURE:**

a. A♭ Major

BEAD

d. A Major

b. the relative melodic minor of A♭ Major

Should be ↑ ↓ ♮

e. the relative melodic minor of A Major

F#

c. the tonic harmonic minor of A♭ Major A♭ −

BEADGCF

C♭

f. the tonic harmonic minor of   A Major   a min

10   **3. (i)** Name the **ACCIDENTALS** of the following melody.
       (ii) Rewrite the melody, using a **KEY SIGNATURE** and name the **KEY.**

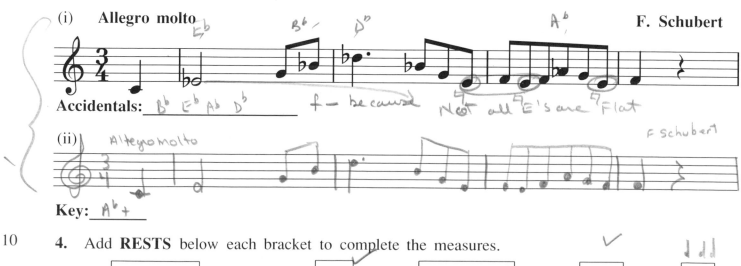

Accidentals: B♭ E♭ A♭ D♭   f − because Not all E's are Flat

Key: A♭ +

10   **4.** Add **RESTS** below each bracket to complete the measures.

10   **5.** Write **HARMONIC** intervals above the given notes.

a.

Major 7   Augmented 3   diminished 4   minor 2   Augmented 6

b. INVERT the above intervals and rename them.

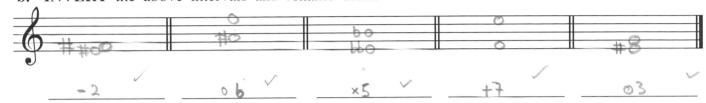

_-2 ✓   0 b ✓   x5 ✓   +7 ✓   03 ✓_

15   **6.** State the **ROOT, KIND** (Major or minor) and **POSITION** of the following triads.

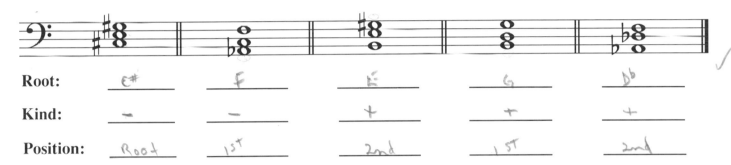

Root: E#   F   E   G   Db

Kind: -   -   +   +   +

Position: Root   1st   2nd   1ST   2nd

15   **7.** Name the **MAJOR** key and the **Minor** key for each of the following key signatures.

B+ ✓   Gb+ ✓   F#+ ✓   cb+ ✓   c#+ ✓

G#- ✓   Eb-   b#- ✓   ab- ✓   g#- ✓

5   **8.** Add a **TIME SIGNATURE** to the beginning of each staff.

a.   **Germany**

         Andante con Variazioni   **L. van Beethoven**

b.

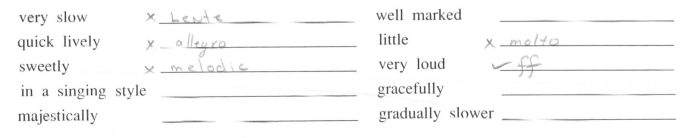

10   **9.** Write a **SIGN** or **ITALIAN TERM** for each of the following.

very slow	x Lente	well marked	
quick lively	x allegro	little	x molto
sweetly	x melodic	very loud	✓ ff
in a singing style		gracefully	
majestically		gradually slower	

LESSON No. 9

Cadences
The Perfect Cadence

A **CADENCE** is like a musical punctuation. It is a **TWO - CHORD** solution at the end of a phrase or musical composition. Cadences are built on the **PRIMARY TRIADS: I, IV** and **V**.

The **PERFECT CADENCE** uses the notes of **TRIADS** built on the Tonic and Dominant notes of the scale.

I   IV V

Key: F Major   V

Note Names: C C E G   F F A C

1. Write the note names of the Tonic and Dominant Triads.

2. Write the **ROOT** of each triad in the bass clef.

Note Names: C C E G   F F A C

3. Then write the **NOTE IN COMMON** in the treble clef, in the **SAME SPACE** or on the **SAME LINE**.

Both chords.

Note Names: C C E G   F F A C

4. Then add the remaining notes of the triads **BELOW** the notes in common.
   Notice how the **ROOT** is **DOUBLED** in both chords.

OR

Note Names: C C E G   F F A C

5. Write the note in common in the middle and write one note **ABOVE** and one note **BELOW**.

1st

OR

Note Names: C C E G   F F A C

6. Write the note in common at the bottom and write the other notes **ABOVE**.

2nd

note in commom stays in the same Place in both chord eg if at the top both chords stay at Top

Note Names: C C E G   F F A C

EXERCISES:

Be sure to **MEMORIZE** the different uses of **RESTS** in **CADENCES.**

1. Name the **KEY** and circle the **NOTES IN COMMON.**

Add the **MISSING NOTES** to the following Perfect Cadences, in Major Keys.

a.

Key: G Major   V   I

Note Names: D D F♯ A   G G B D

b.

Key: Bb+   V   I

Note Names: F F A C   B♭ B♭ D F

c.

Key: A♭+   V   I

Note Names: E♭ E♭ G B♭   A♭ A♭ C E♭

d.

Key: E+   V   I

Note Names: B B D♯ F♯   E E G♯ B

e.

Key: C♯+   V   I

Note Names: G♯ G♯ B♯ D♯   C♯ C♯ E♯ G♯

f.

Key: C+   V   I

Note Names: G G B D   C C E G

g.

Key: c♭+   V   I

Note Names: G♭ G♭ B♭ D♭   C♭ C♭ E♭ G♭

h.

Key: B+   V   I

Note Names: F♯ F♯ A♯ C♯   B B D♯ F♯

Dom in same position

i.

Key: __F#+__   V   I

Note Names: C♯ C♯ E♯ G♯   F♯ F♯ A♯ C♯

j.

Key: __Gb+__   V   I

Note Names: D♭ D♭ F A♭   G♭ G♭ B♭ D♭

k.

Key: __Db+__   V   I

Note Names: A♭ A♭ C E♭   D♭ D♭ F A♭

l.

Key: __A+__   V   I

Note Names: E E G♯ B   A A C♯ E

m.

Key: __D+__   V   I

Note Names: A A C♯ E   D D F♯ A

n.

Key: __Eb+__   V   I

Note Names: B♭ B♭ D F   E♭ E♭ G B♭

o.

Key: __F__   V   I

Note Names: C C E G   F F A C

p.

Key: __G+__   V   I

Note Names: D D F♯ A   G G B D

Remember to **RAISE** the **LEADING NOTE** by a chromatic semitone in a **DOMINANT MINOR TRIAD**. Always write in the **SYMBOLS (V - I)**.

2. Write a **PERFECT CADENCE** for each given key, using a **KEY SIGNATURE**. **NAME** the notes and circle the **LEADING NOTE**.

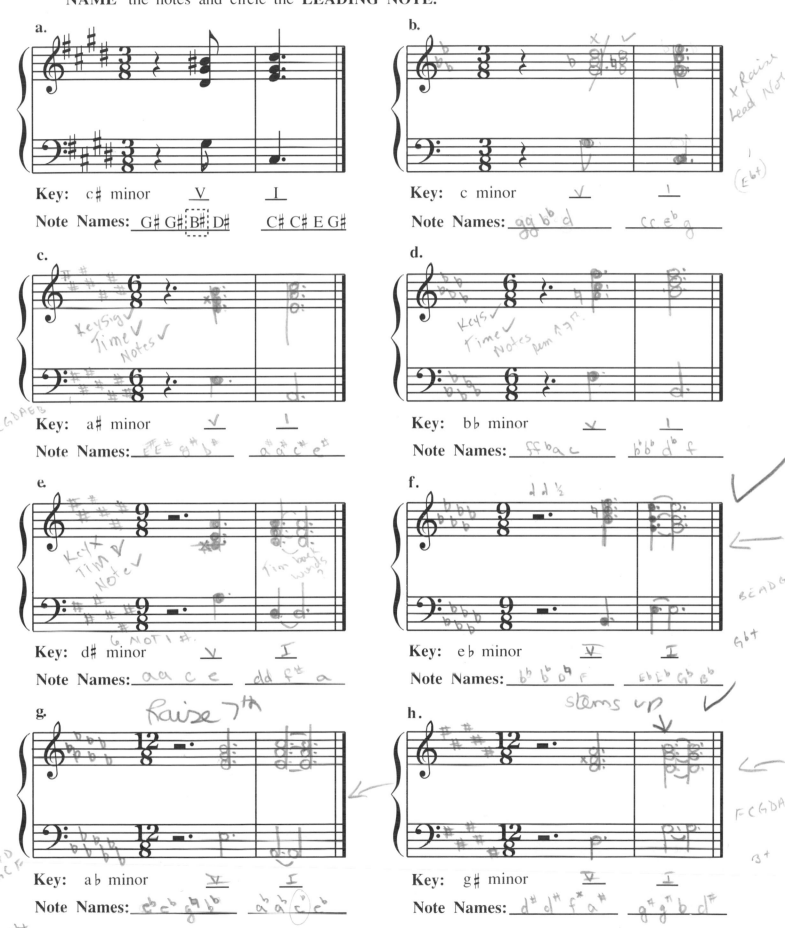

a.

Key: c♯ minor   V   I

Note Names: G♯ G♯ B♯ D♯   C♯ C♯ E G♯

b.

Key: c minor   V   I

Note Names: g g b♭ d   c c e♭ g

x Raise
Lead Note

(E♭+)

c.

Keysign ✓
Time ✓
Notes ✓

FCGDAEB

Key: a♯ minor   ✓   I

Note Names: E E♯ g♯ b♯   a a c♯ e♯

d.

Keys ✓
Time ✓
Notes Rem Ag R.

Key: b♭ minor   V   I

Note Names: f f b♭ c   b♭ b♭ d♭ f

e.

Key ✓
Time ✓
Note ✓

6 NOT 1 ♯.

Tim back words

Key: d♯ minor   V   I

Note Names: a a c e   d d f♯ a

f.

d d ½

BEADGC

G♭+

Key: e♭ minor   V   I

Note Names: b♭ b♭ d♮ F   E♭ b♭ G♭ b♭

stems up

g.

Raise 7th

BEAD
GCF

C♭+

Key: a♭ minor   V   I

Note Names: e♭ e♭ g♮ b♭   a♭ a♭ c♭ e♭

h.

FCGDA

B+

Key: g♯ minor   V   I

Note Names: d♯ d♯ f♯ a♯   g♯ g♯ b d♯

The Plagal Cadence

The **PLAGAL CADENCE** uses the notes of **TRIADS** built on the Tonic and Subdominant notes of the scale:

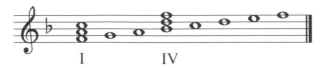

I   IV

Key: F Major   IV   I
Note Names: Bb Bb D F   F F A C

1. Write the note names of the Tonic and Subdominant Triads.

2. Write the **ROOT** of each triad in the bass clef.

Note Names: Bb Bb D F   F F A C

3. Then write the **NOTE IN COMMON** in the treble clef, in the **SAME SPACE** or on the **SAME LINE.**

Note Names: Bb Bb D F   F F A C

4. Then add the remaining notes of the triads **ABOVE** the notes in common.
   Notice how the **ROOT** is **DOUBLED** in both chords.

OR

Note Names: Bb Bb D F   F F A C

5. Write the note in common in the **MIDDLE** and write one note **ABOVE** and one note **BELOW.**

OR

Note Names: Bb Bb D F   F F A C

6. Write the note in common at the **TOP** and write the other notes of the triad **BELOW.**

EXERCISES:

3. Write a **PLAGAL CADENCE** for each given key, using **ACCIDENTALS**.
NAME the notes and circle the **NOTES IN COMMON**.
Always write the **SYMBOLS IV - I.**

a.

Key: B Major   IV   I

Note Names: E E G♯ B̲   B̲ B̲ D♯ F♯

b.

Key: g♯ minor   IV   I

Note Names: C♯ C♯ E G♯   g♯ g♯ B D♯

c.

Key: F♯ Major   IV   I

Note Names: B B D♯ F♯   F F♯ A♯ C♯

d.

Key: d♯ minor   IV   I

Note Names: g♯ g♯ b d♯   d♯ d♯ f♯ a♯

e.

Key: C♯ Major   IV   I

Note Names: F♯ F♯ a♯ c♯   c♯ c♯ e♯ g♯

f.

Key: a♯ minor   IV   I

Note Names: d d f♯ a   a a c♯ e♯

g.

Key: D♭ Major   IV   I

Note Names: g♭ g♭ b♭ d♭   D♭ D♭ f a♭

h.

Key: b♭ minor   IV   I

Note Names: e♭ e♭ g♭ b♭   b♭ b♭ d f

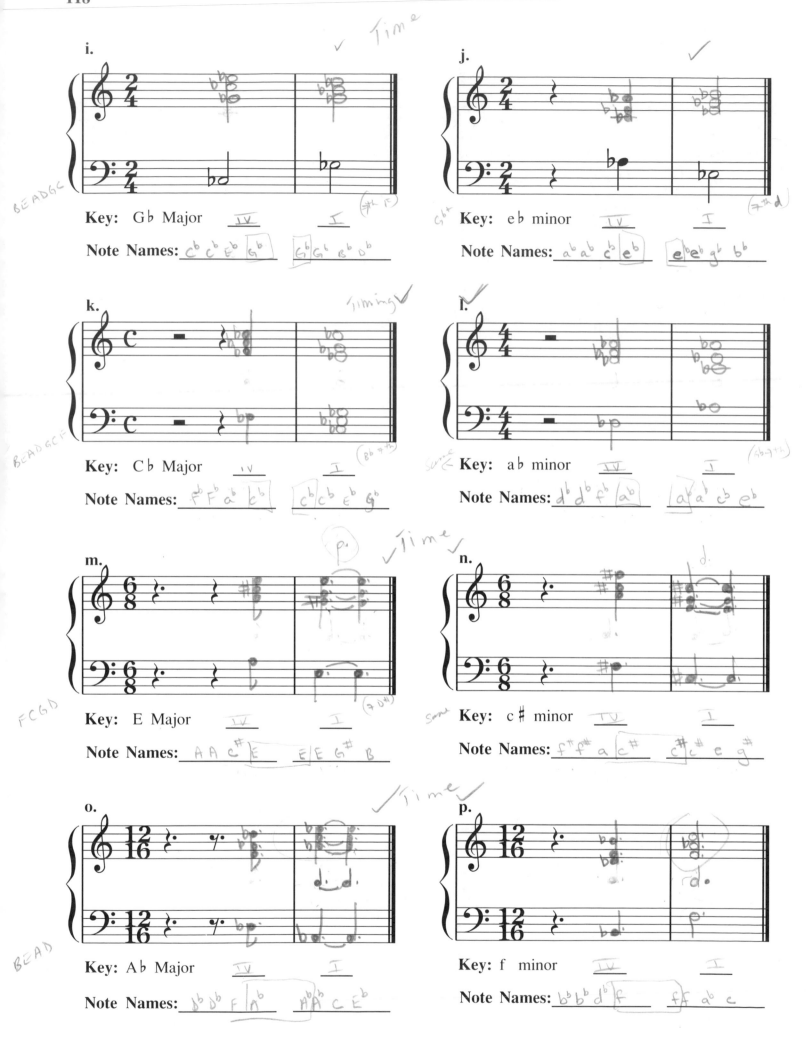

i.

Key: G♭ Major   IV   I

Note Names: C♭ C♭ E♭ | G♭ | G♭ G♭ B♭ D♭

j.

Key: e♭ minor   IV   I

Note Names: a♭ a♭ c♭ | e♭ | e♭ e♭ g♭ b♭

k.

Key: C♭ Major   IV   I

Note Names: f♭ f♭ a♭ | b♭ | c♭ c♭ e♭ g♭

l.

Key: a♭ minor   IV   I

Note Names: d♭ d♭ f♭ | a♭ | a♭ a♭ c♭ e♭

m.

Key: E Major   IV   I

Note Names: A A C# | E | E | E G# B

n.

Key: c# minor   IV   I

Note Names: f# f# a c# | c# | c# e g#

o.

Key: A♭ Major   IV   I

Note Names: d♭ d♭ F | A♭ | A♭ A♭ C E♭

p.

Key: f minor   IV   I

Note Names: b♭ b♭ d♭ f | f F a♭ c

4. Name the **KEY** and symbolize the **CHORDS.**

Name the **CADENCE** (Perfect or Plagal) and **PLAY** each cadence.

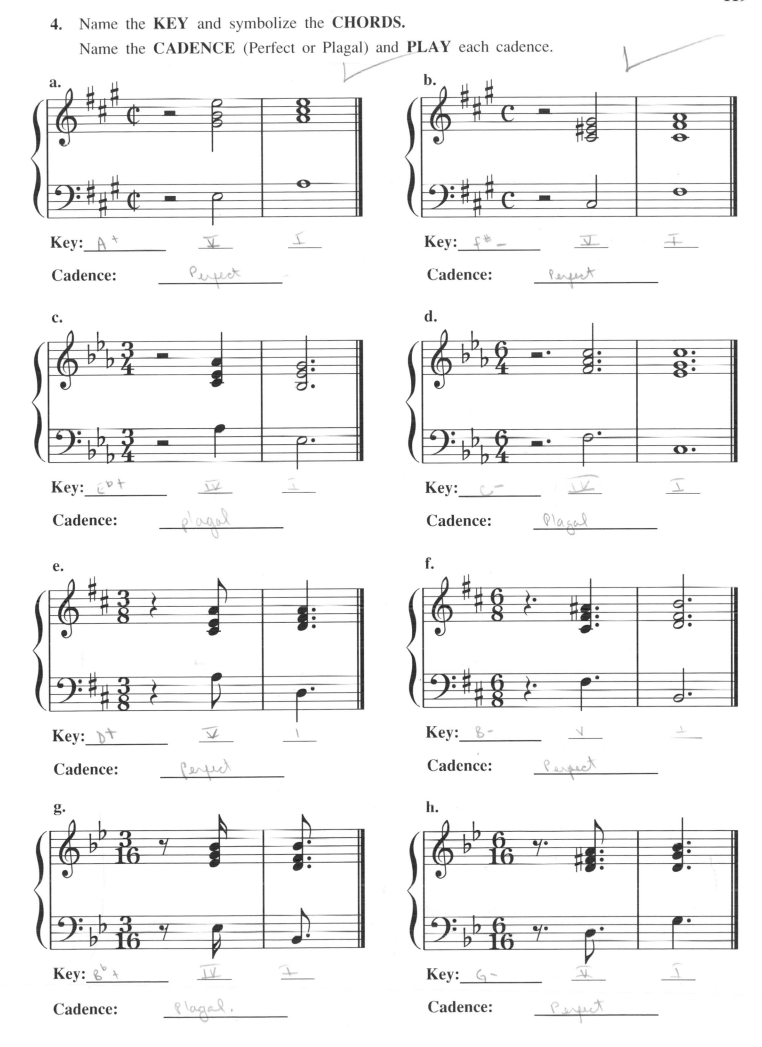

a.

Key: A⁺   V   I

Cadence: Perfect

b.

Key: f# −   V   I

Cadence: Perfect

c.

Key: Eᵇ⁺   IV   I

Cadence: Plagal

d.

Key: c −   IV   I

Cadence: Plagal

e.

Key: D⁺   V   I

Cadence: Perfect

f.

Key: B −   V   I

Cadence: Perfect

g.

Key: Bᵇ⁺   IV   I

Cadence: Plagal.

h.

Key: G −   V   I

Cadence: Perfect

REVIEW No. 9

100

20   **1.** Write the following **TRIADS** in the treble clef, using **ACCIDENTALS.**

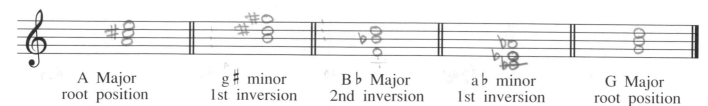

A Major   g♯ minor   B♭ Major   a♭ minor   G Major
root position   1st inversion   2nd inversion   1st inversion   root position

20   **2.** Write the following notes, using **ACCIDENTALS.**

1x✓

eb 7th: eb

f minor   G Major   a♭ minor   F Major   f♯ minor
Leading - note   Dominant   Supertonic   Subdominant   mediant

20   **3.** Write the following scales in sixteenth notes, **DESCENDING** only.

USING A KEY SIGNATURE: **USING ACCIDENTALS:**

a. E♭ Major

d. C♯ Major   *FCGDAEB*

b. the relative harmonic minor of E♭ Major   *C—*

e. the relative harmonic minor of C♯ Major   *a♯—*

eb—mel ↑6+7 start on Eb   ↓down

c. the tonic melodic minor of E♭ Major

Scale Right   Lower ↓

c♯ — mel. ↑ 6+7 start on E♯

f. the tonic melodic minor of C♯ Major

Lower going ↓

10   **4** (i) Name the **ACCIDENTALS** of the melody below.
        (ii) Rewrite the melody, using a **KEY SIGNATURE.**

Grazioso   **Mendelssohn**

(i)

Accidentals: ___B♭ E♭ A♭ D♭ . . ._____

(ii)   Grazioso   Mendelssohn

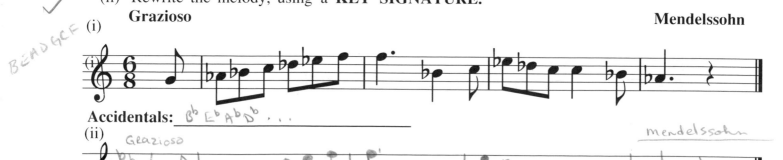

10   **5.** Name the **KEY** and symbolize the **CHORDS**.
         Name the **CADENCE** (Perfect or Plagal).

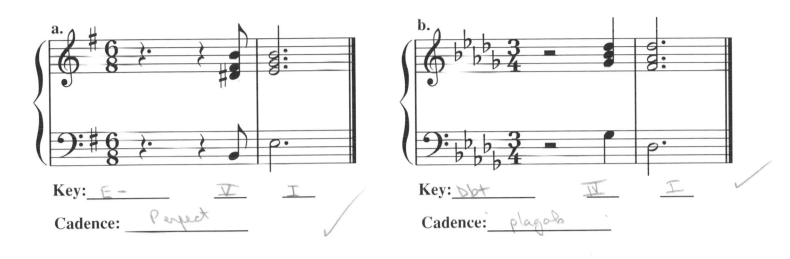

a.

Key: ___E -___   V   I

Cadence: ___Perfect___

b.

Key: ___Dbt___   IV   I

Cadence: ___plagal___

20   **6.**   **Adagio**   **J. Haydn**

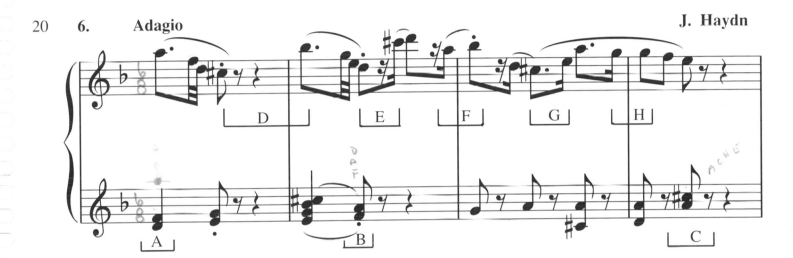

     ANALYSE the above excerpt and answer the following:

a. Name the **COMPOSER**. ___J. Hayden___.   b. Name the **KEY**. ___D -___.

c. Add the missing **TIME SIGNATURE** on the excerpt.

d. What does **Adagio** mean? _____.   very slowly.

Find the following at the **LETTERS** marked on the excerpt:

e. Name the **TRIADS** at the letters:

	Root	Kind	Position	Degree (Tonic or Dominant)
A	D	Open	Root	Tonic
B	F D	close	1st INV	(Tonic)
C	A	close t	Root	(Dominant)

f. Name the **MELODIC INTERVALS** at the following letters:

D ___-7th___ ;   E ___+ 7th___ ;   F ___+2nd___ ;   G ___-3___ ;   H ___P1___.

LESSON No. 10

Transposition from Major Key to Major Key

New key:

Key: G Major

Original key:

Key: F Major

To **TRANSPOSE** from one Major key to another, always name the **ORIGINAL** key first.

In this example the original key is **F MAJOR.**

To transpose **UP** a Major 2nd:

1. A Major 2nd **UP** from F Major is G Major.
   Therefore the **NEW KEY** is **G MAJOR.**
2. Repeat the time signature.
3. Move the notes **UP** a 2nd. The **NEW** key signature determines the distance of the interval.

EXERCISES:

1. Transpose the following key signatures **UP** according to the given interval.

Name the **ORIGINAL** key first (below the given key signature) and then name the **NEW** key.

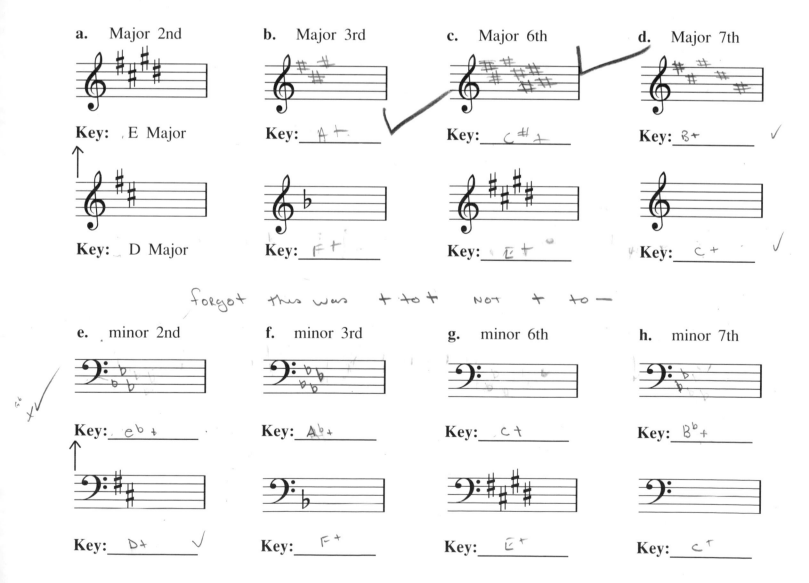

a. Major 2nd   **b.** Major 3rd   **c.** Major 6th   **d.** Major 7th

Key: E Major   **Key:** A+   **Key:** C# +   **Key:** B+ ✓

Key: D Major   **Key:** F+   **Key:** E+   **Key:** C+ ✓

forgot this was + to + NOT + to −

e. minor 2nd   **f.** minor 3rd   **g.** minor 6th   **h.** minor 7th

Key: eb+   **Key:** Ab+   **Key:** C+   **Key:** Bb+

Key: D+ ✓   **Key:** F+   **Key:** E+   **Key:** C+

? tails on the etc when stemdown

2. Name the **KEY** of the original melody.

Transpose the melody **UP** a **P 4** and name the new **KEY.**

Germany ✓

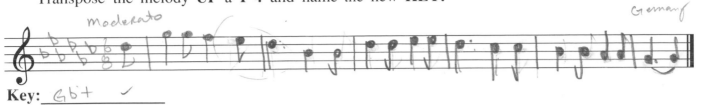

Key: Gb+ ✓

Moderato

Germany

Key: Db+ ✓

3. Name the **KEY** of the original melody.

Transpose the melody **UP** a **Major 3rd** and name the new **KEY.**

Ireland ✓

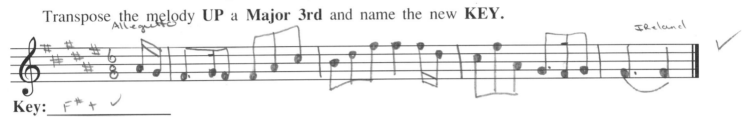

Key: F#+ ✓

Allegretto

Ireland

Key: D+ ✓

4. Name the **KEY** of the original melody.

Transpose the melody **UP:** (a) a **P 5** and (b) a **Major 2nd.** Name the new **KEYS.**

a. P5. Allegretto

France ✓

Key: Db+ ✓

b. +2nd Allegretto

France ✓

Key: Ab+ ✓

Allegretto

France

Key: Gb+ ✓

When **ACCIDENTALS** occur in a melody which is being transposed, they must be dealt with **INDIVIDUALLY.**

Key: G Major

(1) Think of the scale of **E Major** first, then transpose E♮ by a **Major 3rd**, which is **G♯.**

Key: E♭ Major

(2) Think of the scale of **F♯ Major** first, then transpose F♯ by a **Major 3rd**, which is **A♯.**

EXERCISES:

5. Name the **KEY** of the original melody.

Transpose the melody **UP** by a **Major 6th** and name the new **KEY.**

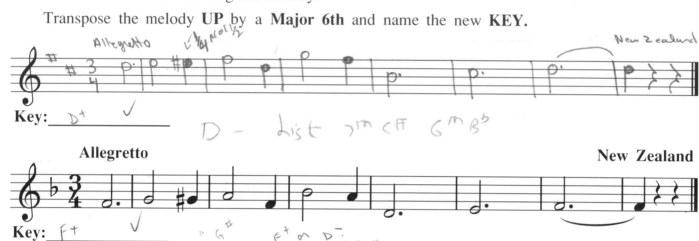

Key: D+

D - List 7th C♯ 6m B♭

Allegretto   **New Zealand**

Key: F+

6. Name the **KEY** of the original melody.

Transpose the melody **UP** by : (a) a **minor 7th** (b) a **P 5** and name the new **KEYS.**

a.

Key: B♭+ (R7th)

b.

Key: G+ (↑P5)

Cantabile   **Donizetti**

Key: C+

7. Name the **KEY** of the original melody.

Transpose the melody **UP** into (a) **D♭ Major,** (b) **E♭ Major,** (c) **A♭ Major.**

Name the **INTERVAL** between (a) G - A Major, (b) G - E♭ Major, (c) G - A♭ Major.

Interval: a. G+ →A+ = +2   G+ - Db+ - ⓞⓢ

Interval: b. G+ →Eb+ = -6th ✓

Interval: c. G+ →Ab+ = (-2nd) ✓

The Old Gray Mare

Moderato   **United States**

Key: G+ ✓

8. Name the **KEY** of the original melody.

Transpose the melody **UP** (a) a **Major 2nd,** (b) an **Aug. 4th** and name the new **KEYS.**

a.

Key: A+

b.

Key: C#+

Die Meistersinger von Nurnberg

Ausdruckvoll   **R. Wagner**

Key: -Bb+

REVIEW No. 10

100

20 **1.** Name the **KEY** of the original melody.

Transpose the melody **UP** a **minor 2nd** and name the **NEW KEY.**

Key: _F_

Song Without Words

Adagio non troppo   **F. Mendelssohn**

mf   < *sfz*   *p*

Key: _E+_

10 **2.** Write the following notes, using a **KEY SIGNATURE.**

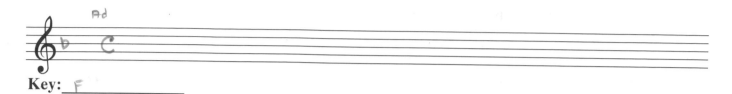

| Submediant of A♭ Major | Subdominant of c♯ minor | Supertonic of B Major | Leading note of g minor | Tonic of D Major |

20 **3.** (i) Name the **ACCIDENTALS** of the following melody.

(ii) Rewrite the melody, using a **KEY SIGNATURE** and name the **KEY.**

(iii) Write and name the corresponding **SCALE** (Major, minor, harmonic or melodic form), ascending and descending, using a **KEY SIGNATURE.**

Piano Trio, 4th mvt.

a.   Allegro   **C.M. von Weber**

Accidentals: _Eb F# bb_

b. ALLegro   Piano Trio, 4th mvt.   C M . VoN Weber

Key: _g-_

c.

Key: _g - melodic_

10   **4.** Write the following **CADENCES,** using **ACCIDENTALS:**

a) Perfect in g♯ minor.   b) Plagal in F Major.

NAME the notes and circle the **NOTES IN COMMON.**

more Note
Below midline
stem goes
C majority

a.

b.

Symbols: Ⅴ   Ⅰ

Symbols: Ⅳ   Ⅰ

Note Names: d♯ d♯ f✗ g♯   g♯ g♯ b d♯

Note Names: B♭ B♭ D F   F F A C

F C G D A

B+   g♯ -

F +
b

10   **5.** Name the **KEY.**

Write **HARMONIC** intervals. **INVERT** each interval and name the inversion.

o5/d5   x4/A4   +6/M6   -3   x4/A4   o5   o3/d3   x6   -7/m7   +2

Key: _____

20   **6.** Write **RESTS** below each bracket to complete the measures.

a.

b.

c.

10   **7.** Explain the following **MUSICAL TERMS** and **SIGNS:**

Larghetto   play slower than Largo   ♪ accent NOTE

Prestissimo   play a little slower than presto   < crescendo

Presto   play fast quickly   ⌒ pause

staccato   short / quick   D.S. return to sign

tie   hold Note   :‖ repeat

LESSON No. 11

Correcting Errors

The following are **SOME** of the most obvious **ERRORS.**

Solution:

1. The flats are written in the wrong order. ✓

2. The time signature is $\frac{6}{8}$. ✓

3. The three eighth notes must be joined together.

4. The dot must be placed in the second space.

5. The tie is a quarter note.

6. The quarter rest should not have a dot.

Look for pick up Notes

1. The key signature must be placed between the clef and the time signature.

2. When the third line note is written independantly, the stem must point down.

3. The last four eighth notes must be joined together.

4. The 2nd D♯ should not be repeated according to the accidental rule.

5. The note stem is missing.

6. The bar line is omitted.

Solution:

When a melody carries on for two, three, four lines, or more, the time signature is NOT repeated.

The key signature is ALWAYS repeated.

The note head, which is furthest away from the third line determines the direction of the stems, when JOINED together.

EXERCISES:

1. Rewrite the following melodies, correcting the **ERRORS.** Look for ten errors in each question.

REVIEW No. 11

100

10 **1.** Write the **LEADING NOTE** of each given key, using **ACCIDENTALS**.

b minor   b♭ minor   a♯ minor   a minor   a♭ minor

15 **2.** Write the following scales ascending and descending in whole notes, using **ACCIDENTALS**.
Begin each scale on the **TONIC** note.

a.   The Major scale, with F♯ as its tonic

b.   The minor scale (harmonic form), with B♯ as its leading - note

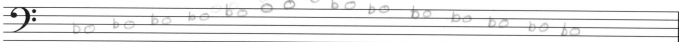

c.   The minor scale (melodic form), with A as its Submediant

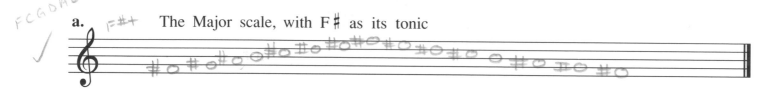

25 **3.** Write the following **CADENCES** for the given keys, using a **KEY SIGNATURE**.
Always write **BELOW** the given notes.

Key: E♭ Major
Plagal Cadence

Key: e♭ minor
Perfect Cadence

10 **4.** Add **RESTS** below each bracket to complete the measures.

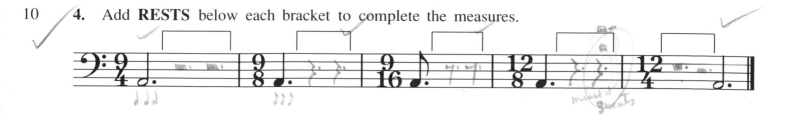

10   **5.**   Rewrite the following melody and correct the **ERRORS.**

30   **6.**

Theme and Variations

C. Gurlitt
(1820 - 1901)

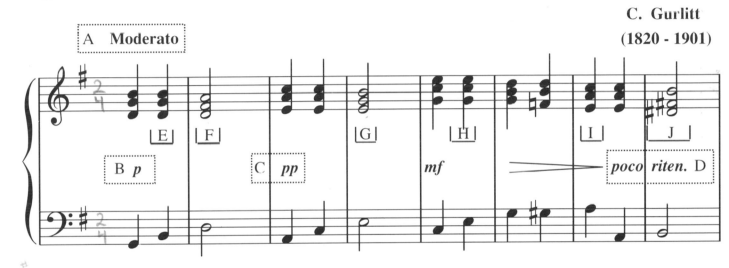

ANALYSE the above excerpt and answer the following:

a. Name the **COMPOSITION:** _Theme + variations_   b. Name the **COMPOSER:** _c. Gurlitt_

c. When did the composer live?_1820 - 1901_   d. Name the **KEY:** _G+_

e. Add the missing **TIME SIGNATURE** on the excerpt. $\frac{2}{4}$

Find the following at the **LETTERS** marked on the excerpt:

f. Give the meanings for the **TERMS** and **SIGNS** at the following letters:

A _moderato = moderately_   B _p = soft_

C _pp very soft_   D _poco riten. - a little slower_

g. Name the **TRIADS** at the letters:

	Root	Kind	Position
E	G	+	2nd
F	D	+	Root
G	e	–	Root
H	G	+	2nd
I	a	–	2nd
J	b	+	1st

LESSON No. 12
Italian Terms

WORD	SIGN	MEANING
Accelerando	*accel..*	gradually getting faster
a tempo		return to the original speed
Alla, alle		in the style of, to the
Animato		animated
Assai		very
Ben		well
Brilliante		brilliant
Col, colla, con		with
Coll' 8va		with an added octave
Con		with
Con brio		with vigour
Con espressione		with expression
Con moto		with motion
E, ed		and
Espressivo		expressively
Fortepiano	*fp*	loud, then suddenly soft
Grave		extremely slow and broad
Leggiero		lightly
Loco		in the original place
Ma		but
Meno		less
Meno mosso		less quickly
M.M.		metronome marking ("Mälzel metronome")
Molto		much, very
Non		without, not
Non troppo		not too much
Ottava , 8va		play one octave higher or lower
Più		more
Più mosso		more quickly
Poco		little
Poco a poco		little by little
Quasi		in the manner of
Sempre		always
Senza		without
Tempo		time
Tempo primo		original or first tempo
→ *Tempo rubato*		"robbed" time
Tenuto		hold the note
Tranquillo		quietly
Troppo		too much
Vivace		lively, quick

Crossword Puzzle

ACROSS

5. play one octave higher
7. with expression
11. more quickly
12. animated
15. in the manner of
16. with
17. lively, quick
19. in the style of
21. to the
23. lightly
25. too much
26. much, very
28. with vigour
30. extremely slow and broad
34. not too much
36. another word for "with"
38. well
39. abbreviation for "Ottava"
40. loud, then suddenly soft
42. but
43. "robbed" time
44. abbreviation for "and"

DOWN

1. brilliant
2. with motion
3. without
4. less
6. very
8. always
9. abbreviation for forte piano
10. little
12. gradually getting faster
13. less quickly
14. quietly
18. return to the original speed
19. abbreviation for "Accelerando"
20. hold the note
22. in the original place
24. expressively
27. original first speed
28. with an added octave
29. without, not
31. and
32. little by little
33. another word for "with"
35. more
37. time
41. abbreviation for "Mälzel Metronome"

LESSON No. 13 (Optional)

Analysis

Sometimes a melody is accompanied by an **ALBERTI BASS.** The Alberti Bass is often based on **BROKEN TRIADS:**

Root Position

The **FIRST** note C functions as the **LOWEST** note of the triad.

First Inversion

The **FIRST** note E functions as the **LOWEST** note of the triad.

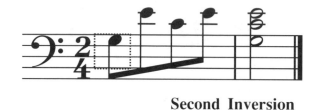

Second Inversion

The **FIRST** note G functions as the **LOWEST** note of the triad.

EXERCISES:

1. Form the following **ALBERTI BASS** into **SOLID TRIADS** and **PLAY** them. Name the **POSITION.**

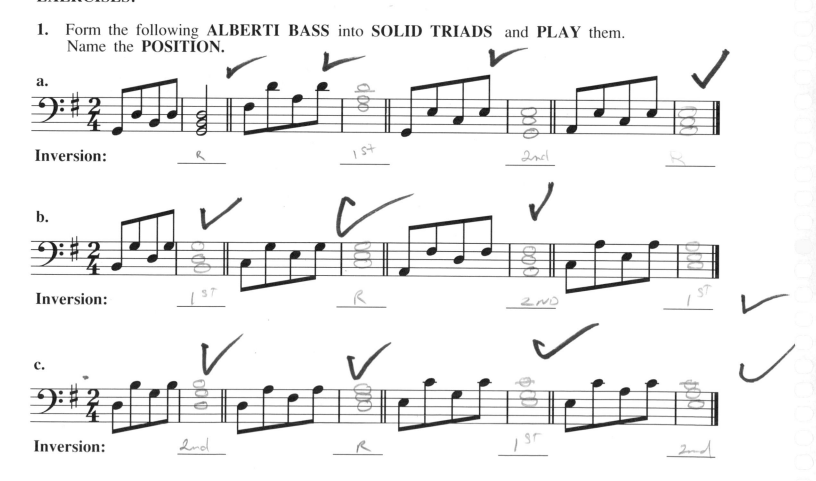

2.

M.A. Vandendool

(i) **PLAY** the above melody.

(ii) **ANALYSE** the above melody and answer the following
   a. Name the **COMPOSER** _M.A. Vandendool_   b. Name the **KEY** _F#_
   c. Add the missing **TIME SIGNATURE** to the melody. 4
   d. Circle **SIX SEQUENCES**.

Look @ Key Sign.
Look for Raised/Lowered 6th or 7th
if ♪ 6th 7th as above ∴ minor key
Otherwise ignore

Find the following at the **LETTERS** marked on the melody:

e. Form the **ALBERTI BASS** at the following letters on the melody, into **SOLID TRIADS.**

f. Name the **SOLID TRIADS** formed at the letters above.

	Root (Tonic)	Kind	Position
A	c	+	1st
B	Root D	– (NO F#)	Root
C	2nd F	+	2nd
D	Gb	+	Root
E	c	+	Root
F	F	+	Root

g. Name the **HARMONIC INTERVALS** found at the following letters:

   G___P4___ ; H___–3___ ; I___o5___ ; J___x4___ ; K___–6___ .

Sometimes there is a dialogue of **BROKEN TRIADS** between the bass clef and the treble clef, as exemplified in the following excerpt.

3.

Pièce

G.P. Telemann

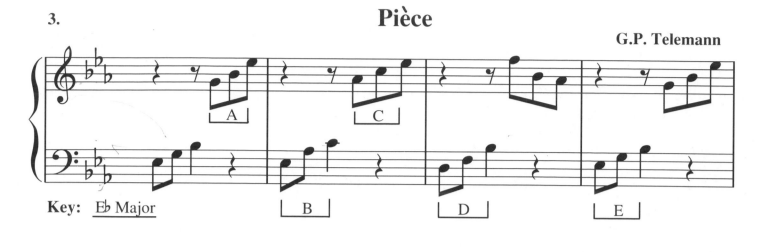

Key: E♭ Major

(i) **PLAY** the above excerpt.

(ii) **ANALYSE** the above excerpt and answer the following:

    a. Name the **COMPOSER.** _G.P. Telemann_   b. Name the **TITLE.** _Pièce_

    c. **NUMBER** the measures. _9_

BIZARRE   d. What **KEY** is suggested in measures 5 and 8? _____

    e. Add the missing **TIME SIGNATURE** to the excerpt.

Find the following at the **LETTERS** marked on the excerpt:

f. Name the **TRIADS** at the letters:

	Root	Kind	Position
A	_____	_____	_____
B	_____	_____	_____
C	_____	_____	_____
D	_____	_____	_____
E	_____	_____	_____
F	_____	_____	_____
G	_____	_____	_____
H	_____	_____	_____
I	_____	_____	_____

Melodies are often built on **SCALES** and **SEQUENCES**, as exemplified in the following excerpt.

4.   **Sonatina**

I. Pleyel
(1757 - 1831)

(i) **PLAY** the above excerpt. _____

(ii) **ANALYSE** the above excerpt and answer the following:

   a. Name the **COMPOSER.** _____ b. When did the Composer live? _____

   c. Add the missing **TIME SIGNATURE** to the excerpt.

   d. Name the **KEY.** _____ e. Circle and label **THREE SEQUENCES.**

   f. Circle and label **TWO D MAJOR** scales. g. Symbolize and name **ONE CADENCE.**

Find the following at the **LETTERS** marked on the excerpt.

   h. Give the meaning for the **TERMS** and **SIGNS** at the following letters:

   A _____   B _____

   C _____   D _____

   E _____   F _____

   i. Name the **TRIADS** at the letters:

	Root	Kind	Position	Degree (Tonic or Dominant)
G	_____	_____	_____	_____
H	_____	_____	_____	_____

100

10   **1.** Name the **KEYS** and write the **TECHNICAL DEGREE** of each note.

Key: _____   _____   _____   _____   _____

Degree: _____   _____   _____   _____   _____

10   **2.** (i) Name the **ACCIDENTALS.**

(ii) Rewrite the melody, using a **KEY SIGNATURE** and name the **KEY.**

(iii) Write the corresponding scale, using a **KEY SIGNATURE** and name the **KEY.**

(i)

Accidentals: _____

(ii)

Key: _____

(iii)

Key: _____

10   **3.** Write the following scales ascending and descending in the treble clef, in quarter notes, using a **KEY SIGNATURE.**

a.   B Major

b.   The relative minor of B Major (melodic form)

c.   The tonic minor of B Major (harmonic form)

5   **4.**   Name the following **MELODIC** intervals.
           INVERT each interval and name the inversion.

_____   _____   _____   _____   _____

5   **5.**   Add **ACCIDENTALS** to the following chords to form **MINOR** triads.

5   **6.**   Add **RESTS** below each bracket to complete the measures.

5   **7.**   Name the **KEY** of the original melody.
           Transpose the melody **UP** a **Major 2nd** and name the new **KEY.**

Key: _____

Andantino   **Chopin**

p dolce

Key: _____

10   **8.** Write a **CADENCE** for each given key, using **ACCIDENTALS.**

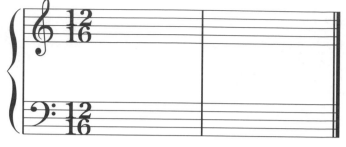

Key: bb minor _____   _____

Plagal Cadence

Key: D Major _____   _____

Perfect Cadence

5   **9.** Add **STEMS** to the note heads and **GROUP** the notes to complete each measure.

5   **10.** Add a **TIME SIGNATURE** to the beginning of each measure.

5   **11.** Write a **SIGN** or an **ITALIAN TERM** for each of the following:

little	_____	more quickly _____
much, very	_____	less quickly _____
with	_____	"robbed" time _____
without, not	_____	metronome marking _____
with motion	_____	lively, quick _____
with vigour	_____	extremely slow and broad _____
too much	_____	play one octave higher _____
not too much	_____	in the original place _____
quietly	_____	in the manner of _____
animated	_____	in the style of _____

5   **12.** **GROUP** the following notes according to each **TIME SIGNATURE.**

5   **13.** Rewrite the following melody and correct the **ERRORS.**

C. Gounod

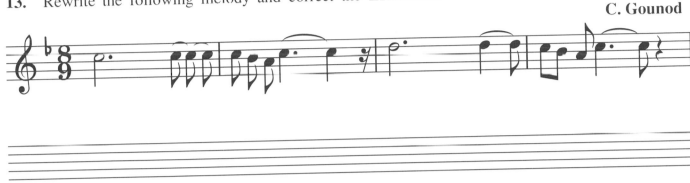

15   **14.**

F. Kuhlau

ANALYSE the above excerpt and answer the following:

a. Name the **COMPOSER.** _____   b. Name the **KEY.** _____

c. Add the missing **TIME SIGNATURE** to the excerpt.

LABEL and **CIRCLE** each of the following:

d. A word meaning **QUICK, LIVELY.**   e. The scale of E♭ **Major.**

f. Two **SEQUENCES.**   g. Two other **SEQUENCES.**   h. A **BRACE.**

Find the following at the **LETTERS** marked on the excerpt.

i. Name the **TRIADS** at the letters:

	Root	Kind	Position
A	_____	_____	_____
B	_____	_____	_____

LESSON No. 14

Melody Writing

Adding an answering phrase to a question phrase will give a feeling of continuity, if the **ANSWER** uses the **TIME PATTERN** of the **QUESTION**. The answers are all written within the octave range.

The answer is an **INVERSION** (contrary motion) of the question. The **TIME PATTERN** of the question is repeated.

The question is answered a **WHOLE TONE** (Major 2nd) higher. The melody starts on a **WEAK** beat (2nd beat), therefore the answer must start on a **WEAK** beat (2nd beat).

The question is answered a **P5** higher. Each phrase is exactly **TWO** measures long. The **LAST** measure and the pick-up beat complete one measure.

The question is answered a **P4** lower. It is best to have the **ANSWER** (2nd phrase) end on the **TONIC NOTE.**

The above limitations will be removed one by one as the level of melody writing progresses.

EXERCISES:

1. Complete the following melodies in two different ways, using two measures for each answer. Derive the rhythms from the question and end each answer on the **TONIC** note. Add the phrasing. Make sure that each answer starts on a pick-up beat. **CLAP** the rhythm and **PLAY** the melodies.

E | F# | G | D | +6 | —

B | A# | G | D | A

F# | D# | G# | E# | B#

A# | D# | F# | B* | C#

D#

(handwritten note-name grid, rotated)